INDUSTRY OF
MAGIC & LIGHT

Also by David Keenan

Fiction

This Is Memorial Device

Fort the Good Times

Xstabeth

The Towers The Fields The Transmitters

Monument Maker

Non-fiction

England's Hidden Reverse

INDUSTRY OF
MAGIC & LIGHT

DAVID KEENAN

**WHITE
RABBIT**

First published in Great Britain in 2022 by White Rabbit,
an imprint of The Orion Publishing Group Ltd

Carmelite House, 50 Victoria Embankment
London EC4Y 0DZ

An Hachette UK Company

1 3 5 7 9 10 8 6 4 2

A CIP catalogue record for this book is
available from the British Library.

ISBN (Hardback) 978 1 3996 0324 9
ISBN (Export Trade Paperback) 978 1 3996 0325 6
ISBN (eBook) 978 1 3996 0327 0
ISBN (Audio) 978 1 3996 0328 7

Typeset by carrdesignstudio.com
Printed and bound in Great Britain by Clays Ltd, Elcograf S.p.A.

www.whiterabbitbooks.co.uk
www.orionbooks.co.uk

'The secret Garden / In worlds of light hidden'
— The Zohar

INTRODUCTION

There's a caravan in Greengairs. Round the back in
Greengairs. It's all that's left of Industry of Magic & Light.
Not the large pile of porn mags. Forget those. The shit on
the shelves. Is what I'm talking about. The shit all over
the floor. Is what I'm trying to say. And spilling out of the
fucking cupboards. Is what I'm saying. Is all that's left. Is
what I'm talking about. All that's left of Industry of Magic &
Light. All except for the contents of this caravan round the
back in Greengairs, owned by some clown called Wee Humie
who it turned out the woman he thought was his sister was
actually his mum, which would explain why he was halfways
mental, Wee Humie. But maybe he wasn't so mental after all.
Maybe he wasn't so mental because he was the person who
bought this second-hand caravan, this ghastly half-panned-
in caravan, so as he could sleep round the back of his mum's/
sister's house because he was into extreme meditation and
had fallen in with a kung fu guru. But the least mental part
of the story is that he discovered an abandoned archive in
there. Posters. Tickets. Records. Tapes. Photos. Clothes.
Paintings. Musical instruments and equipment. He stuck an
advert in the paper. 'Bunch of Local Hippy S**t for Sale', it
read. Job lot. Course I bought it. Course I fucking bought it.
What the fuck is a Local Hippy, I said to myself. I'm having
this. Then, when I realised what it was, I bought the fucking

1

caravan, too, for much more than it was worth. Wee Humie couldn't have been happier, though I heard he died after he got his neck broke in Tibet by a rogue chiropractor on a trip that he took with the money. And I sealed the vault. I fucking stuffed all the fucking stuff back in this fucking caravan. Once I had catalogued it all. Once I had noted down and described every item. Once I had compiled my inventory, and put the whole thing back together, I sealed it. Like a fucking tomb. Buried the entire lot like a fucking tomb and here we are. Tomb raiders. Industrial archaeologists. Forensic scientists. Magic and Light.

PART ONE: LIGHT

PHOTO OF AN UNEARTHLY GLOW HOVERING OVER A CITY AT NIGHT (COLOUR)

You could never hope to see this now, this light of industry, in the skies, illuminating the towns and villages of the Monklands with the energy of making. There was this moment, this great moment that you looked forward to, this moment as you pulled round the bend of Alexander Street, in Airdrie, on the way to Coatbridge, in the 1960s, in the evening, at night, in the dark, when this glow would suddenly appear – the glow! – this great hovering glow that hung over Coatbridge then, this majestic light of industry, and it had to be an influence, as seen from the front window of a VW bus on its way to Afghanistan in the summer of 1967, from the top of the Holehills flats in the summer of 1967, tripping out on the slagheaps outside Greengairs in the summer of 1967, tripping, that final summer of the blast furnaces, that first summer of love, and everyone looking out at this industrial glow, back then, this magical light, and these new towns, and villages, back then, and new music, and making love, and this magical light, hopeful, in the skies over Coatbridge, unearthly city, and long gone now.

PACKET OF SALT 'N' SHAKE CRISPS (UNOPENED)

Expiry date 10/9/1975. Gross.

POSTER FOR THE OLD DRAGON UNDERGROUND ANTI-VIETNAM PROTEST GIG THAT TOOK PLACE AT AIRDRIE TOWN HALL ON 21 APRIL 1969

The Old Dragon Underground came out of a group that practised Noh theatre and improvised music and who were also involved in the early Scottish 'land art' scene. Led by

4

Edward Thom, aka Teddy Ohm, and Richard Butler, aka
The Butler, they were involved in the staging of several
'Happenings' in the fields and quarries that surround Airdrie.

Their most notorious performance was their 'sounding' of a
quarry just outside Clarkston, where they fixed homemade
contact mics onto various derelict machinery while Noh
dancers moved around incomprehensibly, and the sound
was broadcast through a handmade PA stolen from a bingo
hall in Coatdyke. The whole piece was supposed to begin
with the hoisting of an original Nazi flag up a pole in the
centre of the quarry so that it rose above the cut of the
land and announced the 'point of vortex' – an idea Teddy
got from Mishima, or so he said – but of course the raising
of a blood-red swastika over the backroads in Clarkston
was inadvisable, and soon there were problematic kids
everywhere, mimicking the dancers and even joining in with
the music, chanting sectarian chants and playing blades
of grass and performing '*Sieg Heils*', so that finally one of
them shinned up the pole and did away with the Nazi flag
altogether, which for months afterwards could be seen flying
from a lamp-post in Craigneuk, only finally being removed
when it was time to put the bunting up for the Orange
Walk.

The Old Dragon Underground organised the anti-Vietnam
protest, even though, as has been pointed out, we weren't
even in Vietnam. The back of the stage was draped with
American flags so that it looked cool. Butler & Ohm were
playing records; they had access to legendary shit, golden
fingers. Stuff like Impulse LPs. Avant-garde Italian
composers. Drone stuff. Fluxus cassettes. Weird tapes for
hypnotising and relaxing. And they played them through
these bingo speakers. And there was Industry of Magic &
Light, Alan and Tobias, doing the lights. The gels, the liquids,

the live action-painting. Light was a performance with these two. Annihilating light. It was so bright. I remember it was so bright.

YUKIO MISHIMA ON HAGAKURE: THE SAMURAI ETHIC AND MODERN JAPAN BY YUKIO MISHIMA ET AL. (MANUSCRIPT)

Actually, they were all into Mishima. This is a book about preparing for death morning and evening. Also, about living, beautifully, and dying, horribly.

BURY MY HEART AT WOUNDED KNEE: AN INDIAN HISTORY OF THE AMERICAN WEST BY DEE BROWN (BARRIE & JENKINS LTD 1971) (GOOD)

Beat-up first edition of this ubiquitous book. Still can't get over that picture of Kicking Bear.

ROLLING STONE #131 (29 MARCH 1973) (POOR)

There's a cartoon advert for Playboy Records in here headed 'There's More to Life Than Dope, Sex & Good Music', the joke being that the conclusion the ad comes to, after running through some of the other things you can dig – politics, history, sport, mathematics – is that there is literally *nothing* quite so good as dope, sex (illustrated with a cartoon of a 'day-after pill' and a giggling voice announcing 'mama tol' me not to come') and good new music. But literature gets a look-in, and there is a cartoon pile of books to illustrate it: *A Tale of Two Cities, On the Road, Hamlet, Paradise Lost, The Scarlet Letter, Lolita, Moby Dick, The Naked Ape, I Ching*.

Something of the cultural assumptions that underlay
the 1960s is perfectly articulated here. Imagine a 'men's
magazine' today presuming its readership would be au fait
with alla those titles. Being a cultural ignoramus was illegal
in the 1960s. Even for blokes.

QUESTIONS FOR ALAN CARDONA FOR *UP IN THE SUN* #2 (UNPUBLISHED)

Do you remember the first time you saw a light show or
   encountered the idea of it?
Were there specific influences that inspired you to want to
   do it yourself? How did you learn how to do it?
Do you have an artistic background?
How did your first light performance come about?
How do people tend to react? Do they interact with the
   visuals? Do they freak out?
Do you feel you can play the ambience of a room, that you
   can trigger certain states and experiences, that you can
   literally alter reality with sights and sounds?
Can you tell me about some of the equipment you use?
Do you take drugs while you do it?
What is your best memory?

DETECTIVE CONSTABLE JOHN MARIS ST JOHN CID BY CHRIS COLEMAN (MARKED-UP MANUSCRIPT)

Is alone in a room. Detective Constable John Maris St
John is on his knees, praying, alone in a room, praying in a
muttering, droning voice that is hard to make out and that
is quite irritating, it has to be said, and it has been said
many times, about John Maris St John, just how irritating
he is, how obsessive-compulsive he is, our John Maris St

John, whose love was tragically taken from him, and who is praying, beneath the changing sky, in the night-time, as it moves towards day, this irritating man, to some.

Maris is a girl's name that means 'of the sea'. John of the Sea St John, then, is praying, in the middle of the night.

Can you make it out?

Back to me are the only words I can make out. No; *bring her back to me*. Oh baby, please come back to me, he's saying. This isn't a prayer, I'm sorry, I was wrong. Detective Constable John St John is on his knees in his bedroom, weeping.

Their relationship may have failed, had they been given long enough to ruin it. As it is, she died first, early in their romance, and is a newly ascended angel, therefore.

Who can truly have affection for angels Gabriel, Raphael and Metatron? Carol is a newly ascended angel, and means so much more. John St John stands up and wipes his eyes. He is one of these guys with an open box of Kleenex on their bedside table.

The cupboards are mirrored. Are we to imagine, in there, somewhere, entrapped, possessed, the ghost of Carol St John and all of their love-makings? We are.

Detective Constable John Maris St John makes his way downstairs in the early-morning gloom. For it has turned to gloom, now, and the place is gloomy, though in the distance, through the window, there is the dawn; through the condensation on the window, over a newly frosted Glasgow, there is the beginnings of a mauve dawn.

He takes what appears to be a cake, a huge cake of brown rice, from the fridge and cuts himself a slice. He opens a bag of small dried whole fish and bites one right through the eyeball and holds it in his mouth like a snake devouring its prey – ghastly – you half expect it to kick, while he bats the fridge shut with his heel and settles at the table. The table faces away from the light, which means he must prefer to look at these four generic paintings of the seasons on the dark wood-panelled wall than the light of said seasons themselves. We can imagine the sun, creeping up behind him, in order to give him a scare, or to cheer him, more improbably.

He is listening to the radio. Or, really, not listening. He is sitting and he is staring while the radio relays news of a missing boy, the celebrity opening of a frozen-food store, and a boxing match at the Tudor Hotel in Airdrie that went awry. As he rises to make a pot of tea, he catches the boxer's name. Maurice Yushenko. Is Maurice an Anglicised version of Maris? he wonders to himself. Okay, so he *is* listening. The unnamed opponent of Of the Sea is in a coma. Maurice Yushenko has knocked this guy into a nightmare, into another world.

RED METAL HALFORDS BICYCLE PUNCTURE REPAIR KIT WITH ARTIST'S IMPRESSION OF HAPPY BOY WHEELING AND WAVING ON THE FRONT (DENTED)

CONTENTS:

— 6cm × 3.5cm grey felt patch, curled so that it resembles a thin, double-horned tube (pleasing old smell when brought to the nose).
— 3cm × 3.8cm crudely cut square of black rubber (smells of scuba-diving masks and of dentists).

— 9cm-long (large) tube of Rubber Solution, red on white, inflammable, Code 2037, squeezed, expertly, and methodically, from the bottom, and folded over, till about a third of its length. Directions: 1. Roughen rubber around puncture with sandpaper and clean thoroughly with White Spirit or similar solvent. (Do not use petrol or paraffin or other materials that leave an oily film.) 2. Apply adhesive sparingly and allow to dry. Apply patch firmly. 3. Dust repair with chalk or similar to prevent surplus adhesive sticking to you. 4. Do not attempt to inflate the tube hard outside the tyre or lift patch to check adhesion. (What is it about these instructions that is so like a voice from the past?)

— A struck match, its head missing (looking like the old plank of a boat washed up somewhere and now who can imagine its striking).

— 4cm-long masonry nail (seems out of place here, too shiny and new, like it was added later).

— 6.5cm-long (small) tube of Rubber Solution, this time by Dunlop, PETROLEUM MIXTURE GIVING OFF AN INFLAMMABLE HEAVY VAPOUR. Almost empty, squeezed to halfway up.

— Three valves, all in various states of assemblage.

— 5.5cm × 2.5cm rectangle of soft sandpaper with the number six and the letters (partially cut off) PAP on the back. (On the front nothing is left of the texture, but there are patterns like lichen or mildew, black patterns like on a cave wall.)

— Tiny rubber tube, as slim as the slimmest plasticine cigarette a little kid could roll, and with a slight kink a third of the way along (makes a satisfying boing).

— Three small rectangular blocks of chalk (oddly perfect in their shape, two of them at least, like elongated sugar cubes, the other more like the tooth of a dead man).

— 6cm × 2.5cm rectangle of used sandpaper, on the back the letters ASS (really), partly obscured, and the letter P. Now curled over, it takes the shape of a six or a nine from the side. (Paper still rough, with black silhouettes like spray.)
— Thinnest shred of rubber (like a hieroglyph, like in another language).
— The tip of an orange crayon (it looks to me).
— Tiny little conduit.
— Two small metal washers.
— Larger steel washers.
— Thin pin 3cm long (unaccountably beautiful in its scale).
— Ugly stub of yellow crayon.
— Think I may have missed another valve.
— Another tiny tube of perfect rubber (the colour of a doll's skin).
— Another tinier still.
— On the reverse of the case someone has scratched the letters AC.

PHOTOGRAPH OF ALAN CARDONA

Alan Cardona is sitting on a chair. Backwards. I mean the chair is backwards. Alan Cardona is sitting astride and facing front, his arms resting on the back of the chair. He looks like an author. Though Cardona barely left a trail. Which enabled him to disappear so quickly. Which is what he did. Disappear. Just walk off into another life never to be seen again, he is thinking, in this curious photograph, where his heavy forehead, the way he creases his brow, makes his sight seem extended, like he is looking right past you, straight out of the photograph, at everything that's left to disappear to. He reminds me of Chris Hillman from The Byrds. Alan always dressed a little sharper, a little more mod than the rest of

the crew, like with soft, striped shirts with creased slacks
and aviator shades and with slip-on leather shoes. Him
and The Butler had been faces in Airdrie back in the day
and Alan never really gave it up until he came back from
Afghanistan, when he let himself go, completely. It's a colour
photograph that has lain too long in the sun. Alan is being
taken up, now, dissolved in its rays, and I imagine the chair
levitating and him not being in the slightest bit amazed. I see
it in his eyes, in his flipping of the chair, how, suddenly, we
are somewhere else.

ENAMEL 'UP IN THE SUN' BADGE (RUSTED)

This is a real collector's item. 'Up in the Sun' was the motto of
Industry of Magic & Light. They ripped it off the 13th Floor
Elevators, that sun, from the cover of *Easter Everywhere*. It's
that sun with the words 'Up in the Sun' emblazoned on it.
But it was more like the changing of the guard than a rip-off
because these guys were the true heads of Airdrie. They were
the true believers. And they had to put up with as much shit
as Roky and Tommy Hall. Only it was more like kickings and
common assault than being leaned on by the man, in Airdrie,
because there was no counter-culture to crush. Or so they
thought. At first. The squares, I mean. The fucking squares.
Don't talk to me about the squares. But we'll get to that.
The squares. I hate the fucking squares. But. So, yeah, 'Up
in the Sun'.

I remember, man, I remember when I first heard that phrase,
I was trying to score some smoke, some grass, and all these
derelict hippies hung around outside the flats at Holehills,
it was a hotbed of hippies and alternative lifestyles back
then, living in these seemingly ghastly flats, but somehow
revisioning them all the same – what was it Gary Snyder
said about seeing where you're at – and I was getting into

psychedelic music, and someone said, man, you need the
drugs otherwise you are missing, like, a whole dimension
of the music, this guy told me, Tom Paterson – he's dead
now, you wouldn't know him – but he told me I could score
some shit at the Holehills flats, just ask for Tobias, and so I
headed up there – beautiful summer's day – and there's this
fat hippy outside who looks like a fat hobo with nothing but a
vest on and a pair of flares with tassels on them, he just asks
me straight away, are you into it, he said, which was code,
because I was like, yeah, I'm into it, brother, I called him
brother, I felt embarrassed but I said it anyway, like flashing
my credentials; I was older, and I felt unhip, and he led me
to this back court and pulled out this huge bag of grass and
asked me how much I was looking for, and then he asked me,
where you looking to go on this, man, and I said, just looking
to get high, my brother, and he said to me, up in the sun? And
I said, yeah, my man, exactly like that, I said, and he rolled
us a joint and it was one of these perfect moments when the
future reveals itself right then and there, and I'm not kidding
because when I smoked that joint it was like we were up
there on that goddamn orb tripping our tits off together. That
was my first meeting with Tobias. The Destroyer. Beaming
like the goddamn Buddha. What a moment. What a guy.

OVERHEAD PROJECTOR

PROPERTY OF AIRDRIE ACADEMY

I went to my first Happening. It was at a working men's club
near Airdrie train station. Alan and Tobias. The Disappearer
and The Destroyer. They had made these tapes, these reel-to-
reels, I went with this tit Ron Tomlinson. At one point they
played 'Are You Experienced?' by Jimi Hendrix. And at the
same time they were projecting these forms, these amoebas,
onto this screen, using, like, a simple school projector,

these fucking uncanny amoebas, right there on this grass
from The Destroyer, this grass that I had just scored from
The Destroyer who had hipped me to this mad Happening
taking place that night, and it was like the tragic and heartbreaking story of the spirit of consciousness struggling to
take on form, is how it seemed, these uncanny amoebas, these
foetal forms, is how it appeared, and all the time Jimi was
challenging you whether you had really experienced it or
not, being born, wow, I was blown away, every moment
seemed to lead to this, on this mind-blowing grass, to these
lights, beautiful, this sound, repeating, beautifully, this
moment, beautiful, in a beautiful working men's club, in
beautiful, buoyant Airdrie; *new birth*.

DETECTIVE CONSTABLE JOHN MARIS ST JOHN CID BY CHRIS COLEMAN (MARKED-UP MANUSCRIPT)

In the bathroom, in his ghastly pale blue fitted plastic
bathroom, which actually has an orange plastic starfish on
the wall, John St John is shaking talcum powder, Johnson's
Baby Powder, into his palm and running it through his hair.
Why is he doing that? Probably because it is greasy. Now he
is squeezing blackheads, a neurotic activity of the domain
of the neurotic, as well as the picky, and the detail-focused.
What a pleasure it is to excavate, for Detective Constable
John St John, who has brought the dead back to life, many
times, across his career, through his uncovering of the stories
of their removal. Sometimes, in his mind, these dead bodies
wash up all over again, as if his mind were the crime scene of
crime scenes, or a great echoing ark of death, or a museum
of utter carnage.

He pulls on a raincoat – an Aquascutum raincoat – as well
as a hat – a brown felt hat with a crown and brim – and he

picks up his brown briefcase. He hesitates before the mirror at the bottom of the stairs. He walks through his modest rose garden and unlocks the gate. He looks around himself, it's habit now, he's had threats in the past, he is known to some very bad men. He looks back at the roses and he thinks of his father, who taught him how to care for them. Still, they look weary. There is a light in a frosted window across the way. A foggy silhouette is cleaning its teeth in the window. He walks down Craigvicar Gardens, the street that he dreams in forever, and crosses the grass that crunches underfoot. What a lovely feeling, he thinks, this frozen-solid grass that will always remind him of childhood, as he makes his way down the Baillieston Road, the petrol station illuminated in the early-morning dark, the dark bungalows – a milk float passes him – across the way a garage is already open, the school is shuttered, someone in a brown jumpsuit is leaning into the bonnet of a gold Vauxhall Viva, lit up like a workman in the night, so that it appears as if John St John moves from one still moment till the next. The mechanic, he tells himself, the mechanic is to move slowly, John St John, and he slows his pace. He has always lived here.

This walk that he is taking now, this walk to Shettleston CID, was also his first unaccompanied walk ever, when he left the same house, back when his parents were alive, one bright early morning, when his mother entrusted him to his first ever walk on his own, he had taken this exact same route, to the newsagent just past Eastbank Primary School, where he bought scraps for his scrapbook, and on the way back, in a field of flowers behind the petrol station, the same one now stood out in the early-morning light, he had picked flowers for his mother as a gift. I have shaped these very streets, he mutters, under his breath, did you catch that, I think that's what he said. He passes the desolate graveyard to his right, the desolate bars, the desolate wasteland. He loves to say that word. Desolation.

On the wall of his office there are pictures, photographs, maps. Lines of flight link them, lines of red tape fly from the body to the place of its kidnap, and its discovery, John St John thinks; this is exactly how he thinks. The body has burn marks on its hands and feet. The body is the body of a young boy. Found in waste ground outside Caldercruix. The fingerprints have been deliberately destroyed, his hands a mass of scarred fist, his feet an explosion. His eyes, missing; can you identify someone from their eyes? Who knows, they are missing.

His mother said he would break a lot of hearts. John St John's mother did, not the mother of the erased boy – who at this point we have no idea who she is. Actually, a friend of his mother's had said it, one day, when he was out in his pram, but it was his mother who told him, and who repeated the tale to everyone, even when he grew up to look like he did, when any concept of breaking hearts had been put aside in favour of the desperate companionship of someone, anyone, please, until he met his Carol, his soulmate, his cosmic twin, when they would walk through the parks hand in hand in the autumn just like in the poems.

My Carol was beautiful. It is John St John speaking, let him speak: My Carol was beautiful, tender, her skin was soft, her soft chin with soft hairs, her eye halfway down her cheek like a blue fallen tear. Of course you can recognise people from their eyes, in their eyes; eyes are signature, just as fingerprints are, just as a bunch of flowers picked from a field behind a petrol station somewhere long ago and tragic now in the past is.

But this is the voice inside the head of John St John. He is
not so poetic, not so voluble, in real life, as if real life went
on somewhere else from where thoughts did. Morning, DC,
someone seated at a desk says to him, as he walks past.
This is what he is known as here, DC, as if he were an era, a
timespan.

ORIGINAL TICKET FOR THE OLD DRAGON UNDERGROUND PRESENTS THE LEVITATING OF AIRDRIE TOWN HALL AS A MEANS TO PEACE AND OUT OF VIETNAM

The Old Dragon Underground organised this psychic rally
that was supposed to end in the levitating of Airdrie Town
Hall just through the mass of minds gathered there, and
there were live bands, Kommandos of Daath, Gryphon,
Ensemble Muntu, it says on the ticket, and in all-caps
INDUSTRY OF MAGIC & LIGHT ALL-NIGHT FLITE.
They did the visuals for the bands and then Butler &
Ohm played their fucked-up cassettes and their rare vinyl
LPs – *Free Jazz* by Ornette Coleman, Captain Beefheart,
Magic Sam – while they manipulated the gels. No one had
ever seen it before, in Airdrie, this writing in light, and
with the strength of the acid back then – made in Airdrie,
a pair of madmen were manufacturing 'Sherbet Dips' in a
garage opposite Erskine Court – it made for a mind-blowing
combination. I saw The Destroyer, Tobias, I caught his eye,
and I went up to him and reintroduced myself and said that I
saw it in the light, man – I was off my tits once more – I saw
it in the light, I said to him, by which I meant that the light
was speaking like language to me, like we were storming the
frontiers of our own brains, but he couldn't hear me over this
thunderous free jazz, and of course he was caught up in the
making of the light and didn't need to be distracted by a pleb
like me, and he turned around, and he just said, suck it up,

17

brother, that's all he said, and he turned away. Suck it up, he said. Words to live by.

Kommandos of Daath were as amazing as everyone says they were. Their guitarist – whose name was Jesus and who came from Whinhall – was the greatest guitarist I have ever seen in real life; think Cipollina, Garcia, that high, tremulous sound, constantly peaking, and they would jam and they would get out deep, and they barely used any F/X, that was the thing, a little fuzz and a touch of tape echo, maybe, I think Jesus used a Klemt Echolette, but it was all about the notes, these cascading clean single notes, they somehow took you right out there, and it was the sound of the void, man, the sound of dead stars, man, and of course at this point they had a total moratorium on releasing albums, they thought any notion of product or industry was a no-no, was a total cop-out, it was hard enough getting them to accept a fee for their gigs, was what I heard, though they encouraged tapers, so there were a bunch of bootlegs doing the rounds, they were all petty criminals on the side so they didn't care about money, they were eating food out of the bins round the back of Fine Fare, at the Gartlea bus station, plus Jesus was this electronics freak who built his own amplifier modelled after Cipollina's after seeing a picture of it in *Rolling Stone* and it blew his fucking mind.

He was supposed to have got Cipollina's phone number from the writer Paul Williams, who he used to correspond with, and supposedly he called up Cipollina in San Francisco and warned him to 'stay away from my turf'; this was when Cipollina was planning on touring with those awful Welsh hippies, Man. Plus they played a gig, Kommandos of Daath, at Clarkston Primary School, in the gym hall; everybody that was there formed a band, that's what they say, and it's true that a lot of the players that went on to make up

Airdrie's post-punk scene were in the audience that day, the amazed audience, it's fair to say, the stunned audience, more appropriately, that day in 1970, I think it was, April 1970, it must have been, one of the kids just wrote them a letter and asked them to play and they turned up and played this forty-five-minute instrumental based on a theme from Pharaoh Sanders, then a cover of 'It's Cold Outside' by The Choir, I mean, I've no idea why he was called Jesus 'cause he was one irreligious motherfucker.

He published this fanzine with Teddy Ohm that was called *Archive of Sticky Buns* and was all about weirdo British psych records; they were massively into all of that Toytown shit back then, you know, fucking World of Oz and fucking Clover, fucking weird-ass sick children's songs with mad F/X made by blokes that looked like fucking labourers dressed up as women. That was totally his scene, that and the West Coast shit. Though Jesus and Teddy looked more like fucked-up bikers, like Hells Angels. Everybody used to joke that Teddy looked like Cher, he had the exact same haircut, but obviously never to his face, as the motherfucker would murder you as soon as look at you, was his vibe.

I don't remember Gryphon at all, I think maybe they were like Jethro Tull? Maybe they came from Coatdyke? I think in the end they did succeed in levitating the Town Hall, but maybe only by about an inch, and only for a few minutes, so it was hard to prove.

ORIGINAL FANZINE *AIRDRIE OMPHALOS* FEATURING AN INTERVIEW WITH THE OLD DRAGON UNDERGROUND (VG+)

Interviewer: What are your influences?

The Butler: The Who. Carl Jung. Krayons. Alan Watts. Joseph Campbell. Electricity. Carlo Suarès. Dickie Peterson. The Godz. Harry Smith. Christopher Maclaine. The Monarchs of the Night Time.

Teddy Ohm: Cave art.

Interviewer: Cave art?

Teddy Ohm: Yeah, groover, the first true heads were cave artists. Caves were like the toilets at a rock club to these motherfuckers.

BROWN DUFFLE COAT

This is a real find, I told myself. There was all this mad handwritten correspondence in the pocket. But it turned out to be Wee Humie's.

BROKEN MIRROR

Mirrors. They used a lot of mirrors. They had this place like a workshop, like a control centre, this place that used to be a working men's club, down some backstreet in Airdrie, the set-up was they had mirrors over three walls and on the ceiling, and on the fourth wall they had these black drapes hung up, and they would stand behind the drapes, with just the projector sticking out, and they would experiment with drugs and visuals. The audience would go into the room, it's so weird but back then no one was really drinking much at gigs, there was no bar, but everyone was loaded on psychedelics, and they would just freak; dance like maniacs (Butler & Ohm would DJ), make out, lie on the floor like a foetus, regress through past lives, cry, stand catatonic, make shapes in the

lights and the mirrors, try to steal the equipment, hit on girls –
and guys – and they would play their own weird cut-up reel-to-
reels; back then we were starting to hear about Burroughs and
Gysin in Airdrie, and their experiments with consciousness, and
come to think of it, didn't Burroughs and Gysin experiment
with mirrors, wasn't this at the Beat Hotel, maybe, where they
would take turns sitting in front of a mirror and staring at
themselves – hours, days – what is in there, who is that, and
the other one would pass them food and water from the other
side but never intrude on this single mirror until they felt their
consciousness, active, and *out there*, not *in here*, and that's
the same feeling you got in The Abyss, they called it, stepping
into The Abyss, after Baudelaire's whole thing about the thirst
of the abyss having no end, and I heard a story about Alan
Cardona growing up, how he would walk around Airdrie with
this small hand-mirror that he would hold face-up in the palm
of his hand when he was out walking, so that it felt like every
footstep he took was striding through the clouds and there the
sky was, down below. He was the first person I ever knew to
call himself a Buddhist.

UNKNOWN NEWSPAPER CUTTING DATED 14 FEB 1969

Two months on from the unexplained disappearance of
Caldercruix teenager Peter McCloud, police have issued
a further appeal for witnesses. McCloud was travelling
home from Edinburgh in December of last year but failed
to arrive. His car was found in an off-road near Avonbridge.
It appeared to have been involved in a one-vehicle collision.
All of his belongings were found intact on the back seat. In
addition, he appeared to have stripped naked, as the clothes
he was last seen in were strewn about the ground and the
car. There were no signs of assault or force at the scene.
Local rivers and reservoirs have been dredged, but no body
has been recovered, and there remains not a single witness.

His parents ask that if he is alive and well that he please get in touch, and please come home, and that everything can be forgiven, and that they love and care for him so much. When asked if there was any theory as to why he might have stripped naked, in the wintertime, outside Caldercruix, a police spokesmen said that in delirious cases of pneumonia the body can appear to be burning up. Of course, he added, we're living in the world of the flower power these days, so anything goes.

DETECTIVE CONSTABLE JOHN MARIS ST JOHN CID BY CHRIS COLEMAN (MARKED-UP MANUSCRIPT)

A timespan. We are given this span and no other. We are given these autumns to walk in. His secretary, Liz, greets him. DC. She points to a pile of cardboard boxes. The Blackman case, she says. Someone has been illegally pressing LPs in a basement in Caldercruix and they have seized all of his assets. Is pressing LPs really a crime? John St John wonders to himself as he flicks through a box of classical LPs.

He switches the radio on, low, in the background. 'Summer in the City'; what is this song? His secretary, Liz, brings him a cup of green tea. How are you, John? she asks, in a voice that . . . in a voice that is genuine, and that cares, actually. Fine, thank you, he says, in response, in a voice that betrays nothing, and no one. Here, she says, I bought you something. It might help you stay calm. And maybe even sleep at night. It is a cassette recording of the 1963 Richard Burton version of Dylan Thomas's *Under Milk Wood*.

He nods, awkwardly. Thank you, Liz, we say, out here in the chorus. We appreciate it enormously, darling, on his behalf.

He gets a phone call from an anonymous source at 9.15 a.m.
I've got a story to tell you, the voice says. They arrange a
rendezvous for later that morning, outside Shillinglaw's, the
department store, in Baillieston. I will be barefoot, the voice
informs him, when you see me, follow me. He tells no one.
He knows it could be a trap. He has many enemies. Still, he
tells no one. Something about the bare feet has captured him
and encouraged him to shed his own defences. He arrives
five minutes ahead of schedule. He positions himself in
front of the window of Shillinglaw's, a display of mannequin
mermaids, with coloured plastic and fake tails to make it look
like the fair mermaids were sporting underwater together, in
the summertime.

Is it him? Tall guy with the thinning long hair and the
aviator shades. Her? Short-haired mod like Twiggy. The voice
was disguised, a handkerchief over the mouthpiece – basic,
but still. Boots on. Tan leather Italian sandals and checked
socks. Grey-blue kitten heels with a little bow. Basic black
gutties. T-bar sandal in tan. Dull black lace-up brogues. Bust-
up cowboy boots. Grey slip-ons. No bare feet. Is he watching
me? Is he up there, in one of the windows behind the coloured
curtains, a single eyeball, in the crack there, in the silhouette
behind the net curtains, does it have bare feet? Still, no one.
Five minutes more.

But then. But then John St John kneels in the street. He goes
down on one knee. What can he have seen, what is he doing?
He is taking off his socks and shoes. Now he is walking back
to the station. Barefoot. This is why Detective Constable John
Maris St John CID is the best cop in Glasgow. He is listening
to himself.

Back at the station, Liz is listening to the radio. John St John
appears with a handful of raw spring onions that he is eating

whole, including the ghastly stringy roots. Don't you worry
they'll take root in your stomach? Liz asks him. No, he says.
Never mind how absolutely honking his breath is. The boxing
match is on the radio again. Maurice Yushenko's opponent
is still in a coma. Why aren't they naming him? John St John
asks Liz. Why is he always Maurice Yushenko's opponent? I
think they did name him, Liz says. Well in that case what is
his name? he asks her. Liz sits, blankly. I can't recall, she says.

His desk phone rings. He picks it up without saying hello.
That's another thing you've got to get used to with John St
John otherwise it will freak you out when he does it, how
he answers the phone and just waits for the other person
to start speaking, without introduction or confirmation,
even, that he is indeed the intended recipient of the call.
He listens, silently. His strange blue eyes are the colour of
Carol's strange blue eye, the one he mentioned earlier as
being halfway down her cheek like a tear. It is hard to believe
they found their twin in this world, but it appears to be true,
these two unfortunate people, let's be honest, these poor
unlucky souls, born looking like this, and for each to see their
beautiful broken face in the other, and for God to take it all
away again, or for God to think it up in the first place, even.
And here is John St John, getting to the bottom of things,
solving things, figuring out how it all went down. But still
praying, all the same. He hangs up the phone, makes his
excuses, and leaves the office for the day.

In bed, at night, in a room devoid of any comfort, of any
personal touches, in a room completely devoid of the presence
of womanhood, he sets up a borrowed police recorder by the
bed and takes out the cassette that Liz had gifted him, *Under
Milk Wood*. I forgot to say, or rather I just noticed, that there
is no mattress on this bed, that this bed is in fact a single
sheet of plywood with a cover on top, that this is the bed of

a flagellant, my God, and he lies back, his posture, it must
be that he is overcompensating for the good of his posture,
perhaps, he is in this for the long game, maybe, not just for
instant gratification, you think to yourself, and once more
you feel ready to pronounce Detective Constable John Maris
St John CID the best cop in Glasgow, but then he blindfolds
himself, what, he's not going to commit some kind of ritual
sex murder on himself, but no, I suspect he has to blot out
the night, as much as the day, in order to sleep at all, and
he presses play and the recitation begins, and he is back
there, barefoot, on the Baillieston Road, and the recitation
is the life of the city, its characters, its lovers, its criminals
and its working folk, an unfurling as sure and as impossible
as a wicked new flower, and a flower is what he sees then, a
seed point of death, blazing suddenly, and now he is Maurice
Yushenko's nameless opponent, flowered, and blissfully,
briefly, unconscious.

He wakes at 3 a.m., as usual, the part of the night when
he returns to his knees, and he weeps, and he pleas for the
return of his long-lost girl, his dream companion, whose face
mirrored his own.

A good cop is a diviner, an astrologist, a cartomancer. On
certain nights rancour prevails, retribution recurs. On certain
nights great returns are initiated. These certain nights are
when he beseeches God for the return of his love.

He showers – no, actually, he sits in the bath without moving,
just staring ahead of himself through the frosted glass
window at the streetlight outside, and then makes his way
downstairs in the cold light of the dawn. He opens the fridge
and pops a terrible dry fish whole into his mouth and bites it
through its eyeball like a nightmare before cutting himself
a thick slice of brown rice cake and batting the fridge door

closed with his heel. He sits with his back to the window, once more staring at these paintings of the four seasons. These generic, sentimental paintings.

SPIRAL-BOUND NOTEBOOK WITH THE WORD 'HAPPENINGS' WRITTEN ON IT

Happenings? Happenings were happening all over Airdrie back then. They're still happening, only no one sees them as Happenings any more, they see them as crime now, or as anti-social behaviour now, or as just making a complete and total tit of yourself, now. But back then people were much more consciously interacting with their environment. Nowadays, in Airdrie, they are unconsciously reacting. Falling down drunk is a Happening if you planned it, was the idea of a Happening.

This is a handwritten list of Happenings, a list of public and private performances performed by The Destroyer and The Disappearer and Teddy Ohm and The Butler and a cast of people lost to time. For instance, who was this Ruth:

Ruth is sat behind a small table on an office chair in a side street in Airdrie. There is a bird's nest on the table with eggs in it. When someone passes by, she begins to chant: eggs for sale, eggs for sale. If approached and if any enquiries about eggs are made, she names a price. If the transaction is successful, she carefully breaks an egg into the palm of the customer. She then urinates in a strong, steady flow. Requires nest, eggs, desk, office chair, bottle of water, and no underwear. Ruth walks the streets of Airdrie at night and signs the name of the occupants on the side of specifically targeted houses while wearing a replica SS uniform. The next night she posts a set of instructions through the letterbox,

which detail exactly what the occupants have been doing,
what time they have been leaving and returning to their
homes, only written as a series of instructions which claim
that they must be followed in the next few days as they have
been chosen for 'regulation'. After a week she returns in the
night and leaves a cheap sports trophy on their doorstep. Ruth
knocks on doors to ask for movie recommendations. Ruth is
being chased by someone dressed up like an astronaut along
Airdrie main street. If anyone interferes, they are told that
she is a fugitive from another world. Ruth sets a firework
off in a housing estate at 3.33 a.m. exactly, every night, for
the period of one week. A plaque is then affixed to the wall,
memorialising the week.

Who was this Ruth?

PACKET OF KP PEANUTS (EMPTY)

Wee Humie confessed to devouring these himself, and just
tossing them in there, hence corrupting our timeline and
contaminating the scene completely.

HANDPRINT ON CARAVAN WALL

There's a handprint on the caravan wall. Could be The
Destroyer or The Disappearer, their hands were permanently
stained through working on the light shows. It looks uncannily
like the handprints made by kids in the Palaeolithic caves,
where they would blow tinctures across their fingers to make
silhouettes. It's interesting how so many of the now-famous
cave art locations were rediscovered by adolescent males,
Lascaux, for instance, and it makes sense; who else but an
adolescent male would be mad enough to climb down a hole
into the dark and explore around in there?

EMPTY PACKETS OF TREETS

Everyone was eating chocolate in the 1960s.

ORIGINAL MONO COPY OF *THE SAVAGE RESURRECTION* LP (MERCURY MG-21156) (EX+)

Fucking hell, score.

A TREATISE ON WHITE MAGIC: THE WAY OF THE DISCIPLE BY ALICE BAILEY (LUCIS PUBLISHING COMPANY, 1934) (VG)

Light ever signifies two things, energy and its manifestation in form of some kind, for light and matter are synonymous terms. The thought of the man and the idea of the soul have found a point of rapport, and the germ of a thought form has come into being. The illuminated mind reflects the solar glory. A lighted world is born.

HAND-LABELLED MEMOREX CASSETTE WITH ILLEGIBLE WRITING (C20)

Tobias Wright: yeah, man, so, what were you saying? I got this recording now.
Alan Cardona: uh, so, yeah, I was talking about light, man.
TW: light?
AC: light, man, white light. I had a dream, man, seriously, when I was a kid, a dream about white light only in the dream it was called 'fire unsound'.

(crackly interference on the tape)

TW: fire unsound, man, that's heavy; you mean like a
   celestial body, like a supernova?
AC: all stars are fire unsound, you never read Blake?
TW: no, man, never checked him out, every man and
   woman is a star, wait, that's Crowley, isn't it?

*(rustling noise, coughing, the sound of movement in the room,
this imaginary space, in the past)*

AC: yeah, man, but fire unsound is me, it's like, about this
   light, this globe of light, I saw this white goddess in
   a dream, man, this angel who is all in white, man,
   draped all in white, this pure white light goddess, man,
   she appeared to me.
TW: do you remember the first time you ever saw
   snow, white snow, man? It's heavy when you think
   about it.

*(some music comes on in the background, Hendrix's song
about being a merman, it sounds like, like it's underwater)*

AC: yeah, man, I remember fine, I remember fine, it was
   in Shettleston, in the upstairs bedroom that I shared
   with my sister and we both stood up on our beds to
   look out the window together, it was the light that
   woke us, man, this unearthly cold snow light, coming
   in the windows and waking us to our first vision of
   snow, and without the context of parents, too, just the
   two of us and this frozen cold fact illuminating the
   room and erasing the streets and just how mysterious
   is this world, man, just how unexpected, you know,
   and of course my mum and dad had never taught
   us about snow, like, directly, like said, here's what's
   going to happen when the winter comes, but of course
   we had seen it on Christmas cards and with nativity

scenes with cotton wool to look like snow, look at the snow, my mum would say, and she would point at this cotton-wool snow, but that doesn't count, man, that's not preparing you for snow, it's just an empty concept, man, until you're standing tiptoed on the bed and there it is straight out of the future, come land all over your life and smother it, man.

(musical interlude, Hendrix underwater)

TW: shit, man, that's heavy.

AC: you know my theory about how language came about? It's 'cause light is the first word, man.

TW: light was the first word, man?

AC: think about it, close your eyes, you see all those little tracers, those – they call them *phonemes* – those wee bug thing shape things floating around, that is light generating the first shapes of letters and of words and of language in our eyes. Little signs floating free. You don't think the first cavemen didn't sit around basically staring at these shapes behind their eyelids in the firelight and didn't try to note them down or draw them or use them as some kind of example of the way, though they dimly understood it, that light was literally speaking to them?

TW:

(musical interlude, Hendrix underwater)

TW: but what about the white light angel though?

(someone is eating crisps)

AC: yeah, man, the angel is the white goddess, man, and she comes to me and she says – she reveals to me –

that 'our true heavenly nature is fire unsound, that
is why our lives and fates are governed by heavenly
fires'.

TW: no shit.

AC: serious.

TW: no shit.

AC: seriously.

TW: fuuuuck, it's so true, man.

AC: seriously.

(sound of someone lighting a joint)

AC: then what happens, check it out; then what happens is
she reaches into her chest, man.

TW: what?

AC: into her chest, man, she reaches right into her chest,
puts her hand right through this white chest, between
this pale white perfect flesh.

TW: fuck, mate, what?

(musical interlude, Hendrix underwater, crisps)

AC: wait but next what she does is she removes this white
globe of light, bright like the sun but foggy like the
moon, from out of her chest, you know what I'm talking
about?

TW: yeah, man.

AC: yeah, man, and then the fucked-up thing is she plunges
it into me.

TW: the fiery globe, man, the watery moon?

AC: yeah, man, the fire unsound.

TW: shit.

AC: yeah, man, that's what I'm talking about.

TW: the fire unsound.

AC: yeah, man.

TW: fuuuck.

AC: into my chest, man.

(crackly interference on the tape)

TW: then what, man?

AC: then what is that I'm here with you.

TW: where, man? Here, man?

AC: right here, man, next thing I'm right here with you, man, and we are literally dedicated to the light, it's my calling, it's our calling, we followed the light, and I was gifted it, back then, in a vision, is what I'm trying to say.

TW: into the light, man, yeah, man, we're both into the light, man, just came to it in different ways, you know what I mean?

AC: what, man, the light, we came to the light separately?

TW: only way to go, man, what's that song, 'Jesus Wants Me for a Sunbeam'? Every one of us a goddamn sunbeam, know what I'm saying?

AC: good one, man, good one, emanations, man.

TW: you into that Coltrane album *Meditations*?

AC: pffft, yeah, man, what about *Om*?

TW: yeah, man, *Om*.

AC: *Om*, man, they're all like peaking on acid in the studio while like chanting om and playing this wild improvised jam that sounds like the fucking room is levitating and Pharoah Sanders is just blasting beams of pure white light.

TW: the shit.

AC: yeah, man, white light. The shit, for sure.

(Hendrix underwater)

TICKET TO *WOODSTOCK* (AT THE ABC IN COATBRIDGE)

Everybody was totally split on the movie but the one thing almost everyone was in agreement over was that The Who were the heaviest band in the world and their performance was a spiritual epiphany, only Teddy Ohm would say, no, groover, no fucking way, groover, and he would bring up Abe 'Voco' Kesh and Blue Cheer and their version of 'Summertime Blues' and maintain that it was the heaviest, it's heavier, groover, fuck The Who, he would say, and he was the only motherfucker you would take that kind of talk about The Who from, 'cause it was religious music to us, but of course the motherfucker might kill you, he had that reputation, and of course we were all like, I want to live like this all day, every day, free love and endless jams, which of course, outside Calderbank, in Gethsemane, for a while, we did that.

AIRDRIE & COATBRIDGE ADVERTISER 21/8/1970

Beneath a headline that reads 'Drug Death Linked to Mind Cult' there is the reporting of a death at a 'psychedelic rave-up'. A boy of seventeen had taken LSD at an Old Dragon Underground event and leapt from the top of Airdrie Town Hall, like Icarus.

DETECTIVE CONSTABLE JOHN MARIS ST JOHN CID BY CHRIS COLEMAN (MARKED-UP MANUSCRIPT)

Detective Constable John Maris St John has an interview with an eyewitness at 2 p.m. The eyewitness is a hippy who looks like a Hells Angel. On the back of his leather jacket it is written, in psychedelic lettering, the words 'Voco Kesh'. Liz noticed this, while remarking that it may well be some kind of political protest over the opening of a new jail in Northern Ireland. Liz was present for the interview, taking notes, while also doodling and executing rough sketches of said biker-protestor-spiritual guru, it turned out.

John St John flips his chair around and sits with his arms on the back and his legs on either side, just like the best cop ever. Liz takes notes in the corner. Jesus, what the fuck happened to you, groover? the witness asks him. Nothing, John St John tells him. I was born with a condition. How come you're a cop, groover? the witness, whose name is Thom, Edward Thom, asks him. He offers him a cigarette at the same time. No thank you, John St John says. How come you're a cop, groover? Thom asks him again. Thom's eyes are bloodshot; his moustache, a dirty salt and pepper. His hair, it has to be admitted, looks exactly like Cher's. How come you're a cop, groover? Thom asks him, again, and he lights his cigarette. To mitigate tragedy, as best as, John St John says, and for a moment no one is sure if it's an answer or the beginning of the interrogation. Don't you have enough tragedy, groover? Thom asks him. No, John St John says, no, I do not have enough tragedy on my books, he says, I do not have enough tragedy in my life, he says, I have a great capacity for tragedy, he says. How come you're a hippy, Edward? John St John asks him and he leans forward on his chair and Liz's neck makes the silhouette of a swan or an emu or a bird with a long neck and an impossibly small head on the wall – the place is lit up with lamps and shadows just like in a classic interrogation – and Thom says, I have a great capacity for joy, is what he says, I do not have enough joy in my life, he says, I do not have enough joy on my books, John, he says. You believe in happiness? John St John asks him. Of course, Thom says, don't you? I'm not sure that happiness exists, John St John says to him, and Liz takes it down in capitals, and underlines it twice, while a kind of

34

nausea or vertigo comes over her, just there, for a second, before it's gone.

John St John takes out a bunch of spring onions and starts eating them raw, stuffing them into his mouth and generally stinking up the room. Want one? he offers Thom. What do you think I am, Thom says, a fucking hippy? Aren't you worried they'll take root in your stomach? Thom says, and Liz suppresses a little giggle. Something has taken root, alright, John St John says, and he nods, though he fails to elucidate further.

At this point John St John holds up a card. From our vantage point we can see that there is a pale blue circle on it. But Thom can see nothing. What card am I holding up? John St John asks him. The Jack of Diamonds, Thom says, and he shrugs. Not those kinds of cards, John St John says. These are ESP cards, he says. Oh, in that case, a blue circle, Thom says. Did I get it? he asks. I'm not at liberty to divulge your psychic success, or otherwise, John St John says. He holds up another card. A black star. Three squiggly lines like the ocean, Thom says. He holds up another card, an inverted triangle. A triangle, Thom says, right way up. Another circle. A dot, Thom says, a single point. A blank card. A rectangle, Thom says. Where did you get your psychic powers, Edward? John St John asks him. Smoke and mirrors, Thom says, and John St John says, well in that case, you can leave. You don't need to ask me any more questions? No more questions, John St John says. You can go.

Afterwards, in John St John's office: he knew, didn't he, Liz says, he knew every one of those cards, didn't he? John St John's reaction is impossible to read.

That night John St John attends a party, well, more of a do, at a neighbour's house. The neighbours are eccentric, they run the local Science Fiction Club. When John St John arrives, Willie is enthusiastically reading from a science-fiction novel, what sounds like a series of co-ordinates. 'D-567.4/Gamma/Xtrib-ZX952/Deceler D-592.7/Open/745-923/Approach/VXC-222/Degree 29.7/Xtrib'. It goes on. Isobel offers him a drink, a warm can of ale from a kitchen cupboard. But he refuses. There is an LP on in the background. The first Joni Mitchell album, 'Michael from Mountains'. Here he comes, Willie announces when John St John walks into the stylishly sunken living room, hide the weed and nobody act stoned! Willie embraces him, and he freezes; John St John is not keen on being touched.

What are the co-ordinates for? John St John asks him. A young woman, her legs curled up beneath her, answers from the couch. It's an entity, she says, an orbiting spacecraft, she says, an interdimensional invader, she says, and this is like the code to access it. Like a chant? John St John says, perched awkwardly on a beanbag. Like a chant, Willie says, like a mathematical speaking, he says, like a noumenal map reference, he says. Like a magic spell, John St John says, and everyone nods. Now you're talking, Willie says, and Isobel comes in with a tray of mini sausage rolls. Plus a few sticks of celery for John St John. I made you a dip, Isobel says, and she hands him a cutting board with a jar of gloopy green pesto which no way in hell is John St John ever going to consider eating, but still he says thank you, I've already eaten, he lies, but then he helps himself to a few raw sticks of celery all the same.

I'm Catherine, Catherine introduces herself from the couch. She smells of washing powder. Who wrote that, John St John asks, what you just read? Paimon, Willie says, this cult science-fiction writer. Paimon? John St John says. What kind of a name is Paimon? You know it's the name of a goetic demon? Catherine says. What's a goetic demon? John St John asks her. It's a disincarnate entity that can be howled into taking form. Howled? Howled, that's what goetia means, howlings. Does distress generate demons, in your opinion? Catherine asks John St John. Demons generate distress, as far as I am concerned, he corrects her. Depends what side of the mirror you're on, she shrugs, and she walks off to the toilet in her bare feet. Our new treasurer, Willie says, by way of explanation. Asimov crazy, he says, and he makes a loony sign at the side of his head.

Two bodies are discovered in a flat next to Tollcross Park. Outside there is a green Ford Mustang with fake plates. Only the bodies seem to have spontaneously combusted. And left the rest of the room comparatively untouched. All that is left of one body is a single leg. The two corpses lie in mounds next to the couch, as if they had simply slid off, into ashes. Stinky ashes, a very particular stinky, John St John thinks to himself. The flat was being illegally sublet by a wideboy name of Saul. The tenants, presumably the bodies, had given Saul false identification. They had rented the flat under the names Jan and Dean Berry.

That's a surf duo, the guy from forensics says. What's a surf duo? John St John asks him. Jan & Dean. Jan & Dean's a surf duo. No, John St John attempts to clarify, I mean what is a surf duo? Jan & Dean, the guy from forensics says, who at this moment is sliding a paper-thin section of human skin into a resealable bag, is an example of a surf duo. I don't know what a surf duo is though, John St John protests. They are a duo that play surf music. What is surf music though? Listen, you ever heard The Pyramids? The Pyramids? Baldies that play surf music, surf rock, surf instrumentals? No, John

St John has obviously never heard of The Pyramids. So, it means instrumental music? No, not just, listen, you must know The Beach Boys? No, John St John confesses, he has never heard of these Beach Boys. Okay, well, they kind of invented it, surf music, even though only one of them could surf. Do you have to surf to be a Beach Boy? Obviously not. But what is the definition of surf music? It's the sound that these bands had. Can you describe the sound? And here the guy from forensics has struck gold and he lets out a gasp as he slowly draws a single blackened tooth from the ash of a carbonated jaw. It's quite, uh, what's the word, not strummy, but like, what's the word, like, like a kind of fast tremolo sound on the guitars, what's the word? John St John shakes his head, he has no idea of the word. Is that an ear? John St John says, and he points to what looks like a charred foetus or a terrible fleshy shell. Yes, the guy from forensics says, an ear, bravo Detective Constable, he says, but the point is that this was music meant to accompany surfing and hanging out at the beach in California, like a soundtrack to the good life, and one of the biggest groups were a duo, two guys, named Jan & Dean. What was their record? John St John asks him. Oh, they had many records, many hits. Name me some of these hits, John St John instructs him. 'Surf City', the guy from forensics says, 'Drag City'. 'Dead Man's Curve'. 'I Found a Girl'. How did they die, Jan & Dean? After 'Dead Man's Curve' became a hit, Jan wrecked his car at Dead Man's Curve, in Beverly Hills, the guy from forensics explains, and ended up with serious brain damage. He died from a seizure, years later. That's what's called a self-fulfilling prophecy, John St John says. The guy from forensics is running a tiny little paintbrush along the edge of the fireplace, in his white clothes, his tongue between his teeth, down on his hands and knees; he moves so delicately, like a painter. What's a tautology? the guy from forensics asks John St John. Making the same point, repeatedly, only using different words each time. Life is a tautology, the guy from forensics says, and he holds up a little figment of eyelash. Is that one Jan & Dean as well? John St John asks. Twangy, the guy from forensics announces. That's the word I was looking for. Twangy.

FANTASTIC FOUR #48 (MARVEL COMICS, MARCH 1966) (G+)

The debut of the Silver Surfer, created by Jack Kirby and Stan Lee. The Silver Surfer was the herald of the world-devouring Galactus and could travel across the universe faster than the speed of light with the aid of a galactic surfboard. Kirby's art was a huge influence on the nascent Psychedelic Light Show scene, his drawings of interstellar radiation, the way the frames crackled with electricity, the amazing star fields that the Silver Surfer would power through, a lurid kind of gothic-biblical-sci-fi hybrid that fitted the millenarian atmosphere of the '60s and '70s, this evangelism for other worlds, other ways of being, and seeing, as the exploration of inner space became something that was practised by kids at large, and not just impossible hermits from centuries ago, this blurring of visions of inside and out which resulted in the bliss of ego loss, it was real, I felt it, at the Trips Festivals in Airdrie, in The Abyss, when it seemed like it was the inside of your body, the flesh of your organs, the plasma in the blood, out there, on the screen, this fantastic voyage we had taken into consciousness, is what it felt like, and this is when LSD was being manufactured in Airdrie, starting in late 1967, in a garage across from Erskine Court these two guys, the Two Daves, manufactured a whole run of legendary tabs – everybody knows about the Sherbet Dips, of course, but also shit like the legendary Vocokesh (there was an inner-circle Kesh cult in Airdrie, no doubt), which everybody was on at the Battle of Katherine Park, which explains a lot – but then heroin began coming in too, but that was mostly coming from people doing the hippy trail in Afghanistan. Just seeing this comic is like a flashback.

POSTER OF CHRISTOPHER LEE AS DRACULA

And the occult too, people began getting into the occult, there was this feeling that reality was up for grabs, Theosophy, especially characters like Leadbeater and Steiner, who came up with this whole mysticism of colour, this whole philosophy, where they painted auras and thought-forms using visionary techniques, like they had colours for things like 'unselfish affection' and 'devotion to a noble idea' and 'religious feeling tinged with fear', the last of which was like a star field, an infinitely deep star field of dark blue with pin-pricks of light that suggest the lineaments of some kind of haloed form.

Alan's bedroom at the Holehills flats, back in the day, was painted according to a colour scheme he called 'religious ardour' – a mattress right in the centre of the room over which he had raised a bunch of sheets and rugs on wooden poles so that it looked like a Bedouin encampment in the Milky Way – with these walls of night-sky blue and then arching across the ceiling, from one corner to another, this great spray of flecked white – this gushing star-foam – and he's sat there in the centre, in a tent, basically, with his bare feet on, and with lights set up inside, shining out, with coloured gels on them, coloured gels that would illuminate secret paintings on the wall, secret colour codes, so that Alan could play the moment, triggering 'blissful languor', 'expectant soul', 'radiance of eternity', and he had a harmonium in there – where the fuck did he get a harmonium in Airdrie in 1968 – but he would sit in there, droning, droning on this harmonium and singing mantras, mantras for the sun coming up in the morning and for the midnight sun that was invisible, he had this thing where he would greet the passage of the sun at the four points as it crossed the sky, if he was hanging out with you he would just stop whatever he was doing and either put his hands up in the air and greet the sun right there on the spot or he would excuse himself and go do it in private, I mean, what the fuck must his neighbours have thought, but like I said, the Holehills flats were basically a glorified hippy squat back in the day, so everyone probably loved it.

HARMONIUM

And fuck me but here it is, are you serious, in a box under the bed, it's only the original harmonium he tormented Holehills with, how do you play this thing, okay, you play the bellows with one hand while you play the keys with the other, okay mmmmmmmmmmmmmmmOOOOOOOOOOO Ommmmmmmmmmmm it's like a bagpipe with a keyboard, the bagpipe is the Scottish harmonium, have you ever taken psychedelics and gone to the bagpipe championship in Central Park in Coatbridge every year, wait, I don't know if they still do it mmmmmmAAAAAmmm but back then, and in the week running up to it, this park in Coatbridge would be like this visionary sound environment, like Charles Ives mmmmmmmmmmmmmmmmmmmmmmOOOOOmmm mmmmmmmmmmmmAAAAmmmm had set up a whole bunch of bagpipe orchestras just to interfere with each other, like these gridlocked drones, these incredible sounds, man mmmmmmEEEEEEmmmmm Ives had this piece called 'Central Park in the Dark', where he had basically these two orchestras play two different tunes mmmOOOOmmm and march towards, and then through, each other, so there was this beautiful confluence and confusion mmmmmOOOOOOmmm mmmmmmmmmOOOOmmm. mmmmmmmmmmmmEEEEmmm and then beyond, and then past each other, into the distance, so that there was

this sad echoing mmmmmmmEEEEEEmmmmm that's
so romantic eeeMMMMeeee eeeeMMMMeeee I would
listen to it, as a kid, on headphones, at night, I got it on LP
out of Airdrie Library mmmmmEEEEEEmmmmm such
a sense of space and possibility in that music, at night
oooooMMMMMMMMoooooo this music at night, only it was
Central Park in New York ooooAAAAAooooo that Ives was
talking about mmmmmmmmmOOOOOOmmmmmmm
only but when I first went to Central Park in Coatbridge all
the heads were there oooooAAAAAoooooooo and everyone
was tripping and just wandering in and out of all the
circles of the bagpipe orchestras rehearsing, why do they
rehearse in circular mmmmmmmmOOOOOOOmmmmmm
mmmmmmmmmmmmmOOOOOOmmmmmm
mmmOOOOOOmmmm something to do with anticipating the
shape of the note mmmOOOOmmmm these cascading rounds
of notes over a still centre oooooooooooMMMMMMoooooooo
and it was so trippy, man, this band from Cameroon
were there, and they were all these black guys wearing
bright red military band attire and with mad tartan
hats and playing this music like berserkers coming
through the fog mmmmmmmEEEEEEEOOOOmmmmm
mmmmAAAAAAAAOOOOOOmmmmm and I checked out
Teddy Ohm and The Butler, zoning, on the other side of
the field, and I knew I was in, had the insider knowledge,
that this was 'Central Park in the Light', because they were
tripping, totally digging it, and then comes this harmonium/
bagpipe drone: OOOOOOMMMMMOMMMOOOOOAAEAAA
AOOOMMMMMMOOOOOOOOOOOOOOOOOEEEEEOUUUU
OOOOOOOOOOOOOOUUUMMMMUUUOOOOOOOOOOO
OUUUUUUUOOOOOOOOOOOOMMMMM.

(Hendrix under water)

PHOTOGRAPH OF ALAN CARDONA AND UNKNOWN FEMALE

On the Hippy Trail with an unidentified female, unidentified because her face has been cut out of the picture to leave a perfect hole where her head should be; did he use a hole-punch? But the story I heard was this. She never came back. She never returned. He is supposed to have met this girl in London, where he went to busk and live in a VW bus down a back lane in Hackney in order to build up cash for the second leg of the trek, which was London > Paris > Kandahar. The idea was to bring back coats and rugs and hippy shit to sell round the Holehills flats and of course they always talked about setting up a boutique in Airdrie, Tobias and Alan, like a decadent head shop up a side street, so as he hooks up with this girl in London, is what I hear, from friends back in Airdrie who he would write to, occasionally, he meets this chick at a gig at the Roundhouse, Groundhogs, maybe, is what I hear, Third Ear Band, something like that, I'm banging this chick, he says, this stunning posh bird, she is amazing, he says, I'm in love, he's saying, and now she's funding the trip, he says, she's funding the whole campaign, and so they head off, to Europe, only they end up in Austria, for a bit, in the Austrian mountains painting tarot cards with some nut on top of a mountain in some kind of Zen hut, then into Hungary, and Romania, and in Romania he gets bitten by a dog, Alan gets bitten by a fucking mad stray dog, these things run in packs in Romania, they are lawless, and the upshot is he's fucked, no concept of travel insurance, no concept of planning ahead, nothing but dumb faith in the future, or whatever it is that's holding it up, and here he is, out here in the dark, with his fucking leg torn apart by some rabid dog, and the only thing that saved his life, because they were out in the dark of the country, camped out under this awning by the side of their VW bus, but Suzy, let's call

her Suzy, I heard her name was Suzy, archetypal lost hippy
girl in this story, your name is Suzy, of course it is, but Suzy
has the mad presence of mind to just grab the pot off the
little camping stove where they were boiling water and to
throw this fucking boiling water over the dog, and not only
that, but to smack this fucking ferocious dog, whose flesh
is now basically melting from him, up over the head with
this cast-iron pot, and it was like she was in control of the
animals, Alan said, like she was this *elemental aspect* of these
animals, he said, come back to terrify them, and the dogs
turned and ran, the whole pack of them, Alan said, like ink
into the dark night, he said, and they were gone, but still
they had the problem of Alan's burst leg, there he is, lying
there, in agony, and then out of the night, like an answer,
comes this single point of light, this single point of light,
and it starts to come closer, and it is like this great beaming
tunnel in the night until it gets closer still and now it's a light
coming from the forehead of some kind of giant man, some
kind of cyclops, is it, this illuminated third eye, and as the
figure gets closer still they realise it is wearing what appears
to be body armour, some kind of primitive protection suit,
and then it is like he is walking straight out of their worst
nightmares, because in addition to that he has what looks
like a face mask and a respirator on, it's the commander of
the dogs, is what Alan said he thought it was, what a strange
phrase, the commander of the dogs, come to exact revenge,
was what he said, only then: that wound looks bad, the voice
says to them, in heavily accented English, but in English
all the same, and then it says; got any whisky, it says, to
Suzy this time, and Suzy says, only if you take that mask off
'cause it is freaking me the fuck out, and it says, again, in
heavily accented English, but in English all the same, well,
I can't fucking very well hoover it up my respirator, it says,
and she says, why do you have a respirator on, and glasses
in the dark, and he says, in order to terrify, it says, I wear it

in order to terrify, and it shrugs, as if to say, isn't it fucking
obvious, and then it says, get me that whisky, and fast, and
so Suzy runs inside and grabs a bottle of single malt, Alan
was not known to travel without several, and she comes back
and the thing has pulled its mask back up on its forehead, it
looks Mongolian, or like an Eskimo, is what Alan says, who
knows what to think, and she hands it the bottle, thinking it
is going to pour it on the wound, or make Alan drink it while
it operates on him with a bowie knife, but instead it just
says, get me two glasses, darling, is what it says, and they
are both at its mercy at this point, it's like Suzy is following
this terrifying invisible script, and so she runs inside and
she grabs two shot glasses, okay, this thing this deity this
terrifying presence says, okay, it says, let's drink to close
shaves, it says, it's all sounding ominous, what do you mean
close shaves, Alan says, who is still, at this point, lying and
squirming on the ground in front of this monstrosity and his
own girlfriend, let's face it, at this point, this monstrosity
and his own girlfriend, sitting there on a pair of tree stumps
with shot glasses in their hands, although to be fair Suzy
has a panicked expression on her face, and this supernatural
visitor, let's say it, this apparently supernatural visitor,
seems remarkably calm, considering the amount of protective
clothing it's wearing, which up close looks more like pieces
of tin and plastic and steel that it has dug up out of a dump,
and it turns to Suzy and it says, cheers, this strange decrepit
monstrosity says, cheers, what is this thing, has it walked
out of some other book entirely, and then it says, to Suzy,
once again, look at me, that's what it says, look at me, and
as it says it, it removes its goggles, that was the word Alan
used, it removed its goggles, and had Suzy gaze deep into
its eyes, look at me, it said, and then it said another thing,
please, it said, please, look at me, without a begging tone,
it said it, and of course we will never know what she saw in
those eyes, but she started crying, is what Alan said, out of

fear or love of tender beauty, who knows, but she wept, even though, and Alan insisted this was the case, even though she never once broke this thing's gaze, even when at one point there was the sound of tiny wings, Alan said, even when there were tiny wings, and then this thing, this entity, it turned to Alan, and it took a knife from its boot, exactly as you might have anticipated, a bowie knife from its boot to operate on the patient, is what you saw coming, and there's Suzy sat calmly in her chair, hypnotised in her chair, quite possibly, who knows, while this terrible shade, this phantom rose and moved slowly towards Alan with a floating motion, with an uncanny floating motion, and then what happened is that the sound of tiny wings came back, the sound of tiny wings and of fast-beating hearts, and this terrible shade reached up into the air and brought down a black bird, in its hand, who knows what kind of bird it was, it was a tiny bird of spectacular plumage that this wraith had plucked out of the thin air and that was vibrating with a certain tone, is what Alan said, a certain tone, it was letting off, a certain frequency, was what he said, and now it held it tight in its fist, this nightmare, its fast heart straining at its fingers, this ball of energy and light, pulsing and waving, was what Alan said, pulsing and waving through the clenched fingers of a nightmare, and he said it was like he was tripping, when the figure leaned forward, and made a clean cut horizontally across his leg wound, and then passed the tiny bird inside, which did not emerge or try to escape as the two of them, Suzy and this figure from a nightmare, sewed Alan's leg back up, with this tiny bird still inside.

When they awoke, they thought they had been to Heaven. I've dreamt of this all my life, Alan said, even though when they woke the VW bus was gone and they were lying there circled by their own rifled possessions. They packed whatever they could salvage into their rucksacks, and hitch-hiked their way through the Ukraine, and into Georgia.

But then the weird thing is this photograph, taken in what looks like Afghanistan, at some kind of primitive market, it appears, and with Suzy, we have to presume, and Alan has a birdcage in his hand. Suzy is wearing white knee-high boots, and a suede miniskirt, and a floppy hat, with a perfect no-face. Alan has a straggly, matted beard, heavily sunburned face, wild hair, a cowboy hat, a waistcoat with a cut-off-at-the-sleeves T-shirt, loose trousers and bare feet, and on his back he is carrying a backpack with a large, patterned rug strapped to the top. They seem in good spirits, the two of them, even as you can see the scene they are creating from the astonished looks of the men all around them as Alan stands there, beaming, it has to be said, just radiating positive vibes, with this empty birdcage in his hand. And with this terrifying annihilated face next to him. But who was the photographer? Unimaginable, now.

BAZOOKA JOE WRAPPER

Fuck me, you can still smell the bubble gum.

DETECTIVE CONSTABLE JOHN MARIS ST JOHN CID BY CHRIS COLEMAN (MARKED-UP MANUSCRIPT)

In the evenings there is a piercingly sad bird singing from the trees across the way. John St John has come to believe it is some kind of warbler, a blackcap perhaps, and a young one, newly evicted from the nest, or perhaps it is a mating call, and there are no other warblers around to answer it. It is the same rising and falling notes, repeated endlessly: sweetheart come. John St John can imagine its song: sweetheart come, or perhaps even, mother, mother, mother; repeated, endlessly.

At the weekend Detective Constable John Maris St John visits the family grave in Holytown cemetery. He cycles there, cutting down through Broomhouse, Tannochside Park, Viewpark, Mossend. He wears sensible clips on his trousers. With his bunnet on – actually his father's bunnet – he looks like an old picture of Henry Miller on a bike. Only this is already the 1970s and Henry Miller doesn't even have a decade left to live. Nonetheless you could be forgiven for mistaking John St John for Henry Miller when he cycles over to visit his mum and dad in their graves, alongside his darling Carol, who waits there for him, too. Beloved father and husband, the grave reads, beloved wife and mother, and then, simply, beloved. John St John is the last of the beloved and has left word in his will that he should simply become the beloved, too, as there will be no one left to be beloved by, when he passes.

He used to take a miniature bottle of whisky with him on his visits, this is when Carol was alive, which he would pour on the rough spot where he believed his father's mouth and throat to be, watch as it soaked slowly into the grass – his father loved whisky – but he no longer brings him a bottle, on account of Carol's presence there, too, who said she would rather not have whisky poured on her grave because she couldn't stand it in real life, but also because deep down John St John accepts, now, that his father's throat and lips and tongue have long fled the scene. Carol had asked to be buried with his own family, so that they could remain together – mingled, was how she put it – forever. How beautiful is that? John St John thinks to himself, and he can barely repress a whimper. He knows the groundsman, and he waves to him from a distance. There is a funeral taking place, in the far corner of the cemetery. The women are throwing roses into the grave, on top of the coffin, when it starts to rain. John St John updates his family as to the events of the week, taking care not to bother the dead with the dead, and then cycles home in the pouring rain, where he spends the rest of the day pottering about in his greenhouse, spotting birds with his binoculars in the garden, eating soup, and brown bread, and looking at the moon through his telescope. At the Sea of Desolation, no doubt.

Jan and Dean Berry have been identified, thanks to their skin, eyelashes and teeth. The ear wasn't much help, in the end. It is two missing boys, Jamie Witherspoon, reported missing by his parents last year, and Peter McCloud, who so mysteriously disappeared two years ago, seemingly naked into the cold. I found two lost boys, John St John thinks, though he has no way of humming it, as he doesn't know the tune. The boys who disappeared and came back again, let's call it.

Detective Constable John Maris St John is making his way along the Shettleston Road in the early-evening gloom and in the streetlights. On a patch of waste ground there are several old cushions, a gas canister, wire and twine, abandoned beer cans, cardboard boxes and various items of clothes. When John St John was a boy, everything appeared as a crime scene. He would haunt these dumps, pore over these urban wastelands in search of a clue, a rogue passage into meaning. Everything could be read in an occult way that would reveal its origins, its circumstances fixed in the precise arrangement of abandoned possessions, like the killer fixed in the silent pupil of a dead man. This is another reason why Detective Constable John Maris St John is the best cop ever.

That night: that night he is performing a word search in a
magazine while sticking his tongue out the side of his mouth
as though no one were watching. He is caught up in finding
words. There is a sound outside. A sound of heavy wings,
beating, at this time of night. He picks up his binoculars,
out of habit, walks through to the kitchen extension, and
scans the garden. He can see nothing, but still there is that
beating, wings, somewhere above him in the sky. He opens
the door slowly, cautiously. There are shadows in the sky.
Huge shadows in the sky are moving like birds, swarming.
Huge shadows in the sky that look like monks, or penitents,
hovering penitents in shrouds of wings are blocking out the
stars, but no. But no, they are birds, terrible headless birds,
John St John realises, and he recognises, in awe and in
terror, that the moment of judgement is at hand. The birds
are making a high whirring sound with their great no-heads
like swallows, in the summertime, only this is the dead of
night, and ghastly. Maris, Maris, he believes they speak,
with their no-mouths. They swarm and circle and disappear,
gradually, like paint into water. He staggers back to the
kitchen, pours himself a drink. He sees himself drinking in
his reflection in the window, a little bubble of light in all this
darkness. He turns on the radio to hear that the nameless
opponent of Maurice Yushenko is still in a coma and may not
ever wake up.

EMPTY BIRDCAGE

There's an empty birdcage in here. It looks like the one in the
photograph. The one that made it back from Afghanistan.
Only what I didn't tell you is that it has been modified. It has
been turned into a Dreammachine. Based on the designs of
Brion Gysin and Ian Sommerville. They had turned it into
this machine that spun around (they sat the birdcage on a
turntable) and that had a light inside that was supposed to

flicker and strobe through the slats at some kind of rhythm
that was the sweet spot for the human brain and then you
were off, in the play of light, entering the stream, but of
course not everyone responds the same, which we found out
when Wee Nimmo Adams took an epi at an All-Night Flite
they had organised, The Unveiling of the Dreammachine,
where everyone had taken mushrooms that we had gathered
in the fields outsides Plains, the hardest psychedelic
mushrooms of all, these things would really just fucking
headbutt you – like that, you know, what you saying? Plains
mushrooms, man; does exactly what it says on the tin.

ENTER THE VOID NO.8 (OCTOBER '73) BY TEDDY OHM (SELF-PUBLISHED RARE RECORDS CATALOGUE) (VG-)

No reserves. Grading is strict. Offers only. First come. No
returns. Sealed is Mint no matter the state of the vinyl when
you crack it. Cheques payable to MOTHERFUCKER Ltd.

The Bachs
Out of the Bachs
Roto Recordings PR-1044
LP

Much more than simply another garage punk album, *Out
of the Bachs* is the holy grail of post-acid teenage satori,
with twelve amazing, original (not a single cover on this LP)
compositions that combine endless echo with totally crude
production values, cranking, spirited rave-ups, beautiful
psychedelic teen ballads, totally confusing mind-expanding
freakbeat genius (esp. 'Minister to a Mind Diseased' and
'Tables of Grass Fields') and the most perfectly formulated
utopian drugs, F/X and teenage romance atmosphere of any
1960s private press. The only group that even comes close

to The Bachs would be Index, but those guys traded more in inspired cover versions than mind-expanding originals and there's a singular, lonesome atmosphere to *Out of the Bachs*, the feel of a once-in-a-lifetime recording event, that raises it well above the competition. The sound on this record so completely approximates my fantasy idea of what the ultimate 1960s USA garage band would sound like that I sometimes wonder if I dreamt it up myself. One of the rarest rock records of the era. (NM/NM) SERIOUS OFFERS ONLY

Butler & Ohm
Death Wish & Blood Stain: At The Abyss
No Label No Cat
2×LP

Dedicated to the memory of The Butler, retrospective compilation of ultra-crude live recordings from The Abyss in Airdrie 1968–1971 edited into a single monolithic drone work that is, in turn, dedicated to Tony Conrad. (MINT/MINT) OFFERS

Alice Coltrane
A Monastic Trio
Impulse! A-9156
LP

Original copies of this cosmo drone/devotional jazz masterpiece: 1968's *A Monastic Trio* was Alice Coltrane's first date as a leader following the ascension of her husband John the year before. Featuring Jimmy Garrison on bass, Pharaoh Sanders on bass clarinet and Rashied Ali on drums, it represents Alice's first vision of the cosmo drone potential of the new free music, building great arcs of classical mass into testaments to new time and space configurations, as well as a furthering of her husband's vision of a Total Music. In the years following John's death Alice has taken his spiritual vision even further out, going beyond any generic notions of jazz or classical music to create an epic orchestral hybrid that combines celestial string arrangements with rippling harps, droning sitars and overdriven keyboards. A track like 'Lovely Sky Boat' with its waves of glissing harp and its outward-bound arc still sounds unparalleled, as the rhythm section of Garrison and Ali ground Alice's celestial string formations with some deep, free grooves. As well as all of the massive string work – which at points sounds like some of Ennio Morricone's more fantastic soundtracks – there's some smaller group pieces which run from void-swallowing raga works through what could almost be Moondog driving The Beach Boys' *Surf's Up* into outer space. Still, the staggering 'Oceanic Beloved' remains the centrepiece, a five-minute séance that works as a transmitter/receiver of the oracular voice of John Coltrane himself. The Alice Coltrane corpus remains one of the central repositories of twentieth-century Holy Music and this is its founding document. (MINT/MINT) OFFERS

Krayons
s/t
No Label No Cat
2×LP

Stunning deluxe presentation of the holy grail of blasted Scottish underground fuzz/progressive/amplifier-worshipping monoliths: Krayons were formed by legendary Whinhall guitar god Jesus, who later went on to form Kommandos of Daath. The group failed to secure a record deal and never released any recordings during their lifetime, but they did cut a series of mind-destroying four-track jams bled straight to tape in a house near Sunnyside Station that have acquired a semi-mythic status among underground psych heads.

This first-time-ever vinyl edition collects all of their existent recordings across two LPs of primo six-string destruction, and they never sounded better. Krayons have a heady 'biker' edge – they had a notorious following of Hells Angels that succeeded in getting them banned from a bunch of venues – and the music takes up where Blue Cheer left off, channelling an incredible power-trio sound via endless wah-wah solos and dark, black dirges with themes of isolation, darkness, confusion, death and orgiastic sex and violence. The closing side-long 'Galleon' is unbelievable, moving from crunching power chords through singing amplifier drone and extended guitar assaults with the logic of the wildest avant-rock. Liners from Jesus himself, maximal fidelity. (MINT/MINT) OFFERS

Doors
L.A. Woman
Elektra EKS-75011
LP

Sealed first 1971 pressing of the GREATEST ROCK ALBUM OF ALL TIME IF YOU DISAGREE STICK YOUR S.A.E. UP YOUR ARSE. Terre Haute pressing. Two-colour sleeve, varnish print with round corners and embossed DOORS. Front sleeve has cut-out window with clear acetate with the band picture printed on it in half-tone, yellow inner sleeve also with round corners, black 'crucifix' design on the back. Columbus Circle address on rear and on labels, no Warner Brothers 'W' on the 'butterfly' label. Shrink wrap has hype sticker that reads: 'Includes the hit single Love Her Madly'. (MINT/MINT) OFFERS.

Fraction
Moon Blood
Angelus Records WR-5005
LP

Managed to score a handful of this amazing acid-punk album which came out a few years back, still *the* ecstatic star-seed-gobbling acid-evangelist biker-rock private press side of yr lifetime, all packaged in a cool die-cut sleeve with red transparency. One of the most outrageously bombed thug/biker/psych LPs ever to blow out of post-acid-test West Coast USA, *Moon Blood* combines eschatological Christian lyrics, post-Doors psychedelic ritual, vocals that taste of jugs of PCP and long, almost oppressively intense, guitar-drenched paeans to personal exorcism. These guys wrestle more pathos and brain-bombing psychedelic energy from a single note than any reverb-soaked, F/X-damaged cosmonaut you might wanna name. Are you ready to testify? (MINT/MINT) OFFERS

These Trails
s/t
Sinergia SR-4059
LP

New release that already stands alongside the Mu LP as the greatest Hawaiian psych album. Margaret Morgan's blissfully stoned vocals touch on the same kind of mystery zone as Linda Perhacs, while the beautiful acid clarity of the music mixes acoustic folk instrumentation – dulcimer, sitar, tabla – with electric guitar and ARP synth to generate a hazy vibe that's somewhere between the most hallucinatory exotica and blissed-out West Coast psych. The 'Hawaiian' atmosphere adds a further level of dislocation, with vortices of singing strings illuminated by sun-soaked drones and odd/complex melodies with alla the brain-razzing appeal of noonday ragas. Some of the playing has a slow-motion Bola Sete feel to it, that same remarkable rendering of geography in sound w/a feel for the furthest fringes of the map. (MINT/MINT) OFFERS

Mayo Thompson
Corky's Debt to His Father
Texas Revolution CFS-2270
LP

Unbelievable score of this amazing edition-of-nada LP from 1970, a striking and unexpected farewell to Thompson's acid-punk roots in the Red Krayola. His guitar playing here is at its most erratic and exuberant, with single riffs extrapolated into baroque cowpunk operettas, accompanied by an armoury of asides lifted from imaginary sepia-toned vaudeville and music hall sources. The lyrics are full of inspired, pithy observations on the minutiae of personal relations, all delivered in an endearingly straightforward style. Alongside Syd Barrett and Skip Spence, Mayo Thompson remains the king of the wayward, attention-deficit riff, with a rhythmic guitar style that wanders into all sorts of unlikely areas while at the same time getting the point across as concisely as the most monosyllabic of garage punks. 'M.T. Oyster Thins' is an operetta within an operetta, a series of tempo-juggling movements all held together by a riff that's guided by the slightest sliver of formal logic, at once a Caribbean love song performed by a toy orchestra, a buoyant sea shanty scored for cartoon percussion and an easy garage punk anthem with a baroque, kindergarten edge. It's an ear-peeling tour-de-force, with Thompson pulling off a forever-mutating riff that jump-cuts between several cardboard scenes without once letting the seams show. But it's the level of songwriting that'll keep you coming back, each track a miniature masterpiece, an endlessly unravelling series of pithy melodic gems that are as heart-swooningly beautiful as they are brain-massaging. I'll take this over *Trout Mask Replica* any day. (VG+/NEAR MINT) SERIOUS OFFERS ONLY

Ruth White
7 Trumps from the Tarot Cards and Pinions
Limelight LS-86058
LP

Bunch of sealed copies of this amazing off-the-wall dark
electronic/psych/weirdo side: White recorded *7 Trumps from
the Tarot Cards* in 1969 in her own studio using invented
or otherwise modified electronics just before her equally
amazing setting of *The Flowers of Evil* by Baudelaire,
which was scored for electronics and her own voice, often
Satanically modulated or processed through weird sing-
song patches and alien F/X. White's occult electronics come
over as somewhere between Lothar and the Hand People
and Buffy Sainte-Marie's 'God Is Alive, Magic Is Afoot'
and the atmosphere is just massively psychedelic, with
aspects of modern composition but with an almost Kenneth
Anger soundtrack vibe and a heady ritual feel. White plays
her own pitched oscillators, built using bathroom tiles for
keys (!), as well as using a primitive rhythm box, a spring
reverb unit, hand-cut tape loops, subliminals, backwards
F/X and various vocal filters. It's impossible to classify this
amazing side, call it black psychedelia, cosmic music, avant-
garde composition, it defies any of these categories, totally
transcending its crude DIY genesis with an atmosphere that
is deeply occult and an unfolding sense of narrative that is
totally gripping. Seven tarot cards are sounded: The Wheel
of Fortune, The Magician, The Hanged Man, The Sun, The
Tower, The Lovers and The World, while over on the flip she
presents a hallucinogenic modular hymn to 'A Choreography
About Symbolic Flight'. *7 Trumps . . .* was released as part
of a world-beating run on the Mercury Limelight series and
was book-ended by Pierre Henry's *Mass for Today,* Fifty Foot
Hose's *Cauldron, Response: Electronic Music from Norway*

and Pierre Henry's *Variations for a Door and a Sigh*. Alright!
(MINT/MINT) OFFERS

La Monte Young, Marian Zazeela and the Dream Syndicate
s/t
No Label No Cat
LP

Grey-area LP edition of previously unreleased works from
La Monte Young, Marian Zazeela and the original Dream
Syndicate: this is a revelatory unearthing; the A-side
presents 'Day of the Holy Mountain Part Two' aka 'The
Overday, 28 xi 63', a live zoned drone ascension from 1963
featuring the original Dream Syndicate with a rare outing
from La Monte Young on sopranino. The slow, dark string
drones, courtesy of John Cale and Tony Conrad, perfectly
encapsulate Cale's description of how the Dream Syndicate
used hypnotism mingled with malevolence and coupled with
Angus MacLise's (whose *Year* poem/art piece provides the
piece's title) fast, rainfall percussion the effect is absolutely
mesmerising, black, magisterial urban/devotional drone
with a unique ability to confuse time and space. La Monte's
playing is phenomenal, generating endless circular tones
while joining the dots between early free jazz reveries,
dervish music and the sound of 'holy minimalism'. The
recording quality is great, affording a rare insight into one
of the most legendary new music ensembles of the twentieth
century at a delirious peak. But there's more: the flip consists
of an amazing never-before-issued recording from '65 and
it is one of the most elementally profound vocal/sound
works to come out of the heroic early phase of minimalism,
channelling the background roar of the cosmos through
cassette hiss, sustained string drones and hysterical vocals
(the piece was reputedly recorded by Jack Smith). A stunning
set, beautifully presented with full-colour paste-on sleeves,

a super-enigmatic insert and nada in terms of information. A salutary reminder of the reality-warping potential of La Monte Young's minimalist project and a rare opportunity to hear these much whispered-about recordings. One of the all-time best selections of this historic music. Very limited pressing, strictly one per customer. (MINT/MINT) OFFERS

Zweistein
Trip – Flip Out – Meditation
Philips 6630-002
3×LP

Already classic European psych/drone/avant-garde/what-the-fuck masterpiece: released by Philips Germany in 1970, this has been almost impossible to source since, but it remains one of the weirdest avant-garde/rock entry points in the whole new European rock scene. Super-elaborate packaging with embossed silver paper and mirrored sleeve. Zweistein are the trio of Jacques Dorian, Suzanne Doucet and Diane Doucet and *Trip – Flip Out – Meditation* is a peerless set of primitively collaged sound pieces, deep-space drones, solitary organ dreamscapes, abstract guitar/drums crunch, acid-folk comedowns, beautiful psychedelic mind-blowers and endlessly detailed environmental recordings. Two hours of dislocated acid-damaged visions refracted through some of the most intensely illuminated moments of post-rock gnosis ever formulated by actual humans. Limited copies, won't be around for long. Enter the mirror! (MINT/MINT) OFFERS

Various
Oz Days Live
Oz Records OZ-1/OZ-2
2×LP

Limited copies of this brand-new 2×LP from Japan. The mysterious Les Rallizes Denudes contribute a side-long track that is one of the most OTT fuzz/echo jams of all time (anyone got any more info?) alongside tracks from the mighty Taj Mahal Travellers (featuring Takehisa Kosugi), Miyako Ochi, Acid Seven and Minami Masato. An amazing snapshot of what's happening in Japan right now. Packaged in a hand-stamped oversize brown paper envelope with three-panel insert. (EX/MINT) OFFERS

COLLAPSED TENT WITH MOULD ON IT AND A TON OF DEAD MIDGES

They had this thing where they took LSD and climbed mountains. In the dark. Teddy Ohm and Alan Cardona. True heads, serious seekers. Suilven, Stac Polly, Ben Vorlich. They would camp down on the beach at the foot of Stac Polly, and they'd sleep all day, and rise with the stars.

The sound of the stags bellowing in the hills, the bright comets in the clear night-time sky, the stars that look like painted tapestry, this is 1971, perhaps, can you imagine it, the air is warm, the water from the loch tastes sweet and sandy, the baked beans and chorizo in a single pot followed by a Tunnock's Caramel Wafer is the best breakfast you never had, with sandy tea to follow.

What are we looking for when we do these crazy things? What do we believe is the result of this kind of extreme initiation, these vision quests? I imagine that we believe there to be another level of life, that it is possible to break through to a more intense, and less worded, experience of this world, and Alan Cardona strips off and runs into the loch in the morning, on their return from tripping on the peaks, and he keeps running, and he never reaches the depths. Or does he?

What is this tent collapsed over? A singularity, an endless depth.

COLOUR PHOTO OF SOME OLD GUY

Who the fuck is this, some old guy with mad bushy hair and a mad grey beard, petting some dog on the lawn of some weird modernist home who knows when now in the past but sometime round 1970, I'm guessing, he's wearing green wellington boots over blue denims and a dark blue jumper with the sleeves rolled up, there are flowers in containers in the background that look like poppies, this guy looks like a lot of fun actually, like an eccentric architect. There's another dog sat on the lawn. I don't even know what the word is for the shape of those windows, is it like an angled rhombus? The dark opaque windows and the white of the building. Feel like there's a clue here somewhere.

SAME COLOUR PHOTO OF SOME OLD GUY

Okay, I found out who it is, I think. I think it's the radical non-dualist who used to teach out of this mad modernist bungalow outside Caldercruix, Teddy Ohm said his name was James Blackman. Teddy Ohm was a radical non-dualist, or so he says. Says he used to go to sessions at this guy's house where they would attempt to dissolve the I, where they would practise all these self-questionings, these interrogations of the I until it was like floating in a fuzzy field of pure sensation, was what Ohm said, but then he said he and Alan used to go to this guy's bungalow and do week-long retreats where they were meditating and doing yoga on acid. Then he found out he had a pressing plant in his fucking basement, that he had built an amateur fucking pressing plant down there and was bootlegging classical music LPs and selling them for a fortune and, of course, Teddy sees an opportunity and offers the guy a business deal because as well as having an amazing collection of original LPs, Teddy was sitting on a bunch of unreleased recordings of La Monte Young and the Theatre of Eternal Music that he had stolen from La Monte when Teddy went on his legendary Downtown New York pilgrimage in 1966. Tony Conrad encouraged me, he would say, these bootlegs have entirely his blessing, he would boast, and so they start up this underground vinyl business (what is it with hippies and these weird fucking basement bunkers).

Teddy said that James Blackman was one of the best teachers he ever had. That he didn't so much teach the dharma as manifest it. He also said that he was only capable of receiving the dharma through someone who was *fatally flawed*. That's how Blackman became my guru, Teddy said. Blackman was your guru? Yeah, groover, for a time, he said. And what was his fatal flaw? Hubris, Teddy said.

Blackman wrote a memoir, *Mahatmas of Scottish Mountains,* that I think influenced their night climbs on LSD.

DETECTIVE CONSTABLE JOHN MARIS ST JOHN CID BY CHRIS COLEMAN (MARKED-UP MANUSCRIPT)

Detective Constable John Maris St John has a witness interview at 2 p.m. It's a re-interview, actually. One year on from the reported disappearance of Jamie Witherspoon. He is re-interviewing Alan Cardona. But before that he is eating a whole bag of celery, which is the smuggest sound in the world, gad, I can't stand it. I feel for Liz, in that office with him. Gad. After all that, he makes his way to reception

and spies Alan reading *A Spotter's Guide to British Birds.*
Alan, he says, and he offers him his hand. Jesus Christ, Alan
says, fuck me but I forget you look like that every time, I
mean, sorry, you just fucking startled me, that's all, he says.
It's okay, John Maris St John says, I'm used to it, which is
another reason he's the best cop, 'cause he could scare the
living shite out of anyone. You're a birder, he says, glad to
meet a fellow enthusiast. When I was growing up, I barely
noticed any of the things around me, Alan says, as they pass
along bland, yellow-painted corridors, like in a hospital or at
war, I didn't notice birds, and trees, and flowers, he says, it's
crazy. I'm trying to make up for it, now, trying to notice stuff
more, trying to pay attention. Paying attention, John St John
says, that's what it's all about.

John St John whips his chair around in the interview room,
one which does have a two-way mirror, like in all the best
cop shows, and Liz sits in the corner of the room, and takes
notes, and sketches. Who is behind the mirror, or if indeed
there is anyone behind the mirror, is pure conjecture at this
point. John St John cautions Alan, then he holds up a card.
Five-pointed star, Alan says. Waves, Alan says. The star
sinks into the waves, he says. Did you ever hear from Jamie
Witherspoon, in the end? John St John asks him. No, Alan
says. He pretty conclusively disappeared. I told you, he was
supposed to show up for initiation, but he never did, he says.
What would you say if I told you he came back? John St John
asks Alan Cardona. I'd ask what he came back as, Alan says.
He came back as an ash castle, in the end, John St John
says, but it is almost as if he was not the one speaking. An
ash castle on a ghost coast, John St John says, in this same
voice. Wow, Alan says, sounds like a killer band name, Ash
Castles on the Ghost Coast. That's all we are, in the end,
John St John says. But before that; did he step through the
mirror and come back? Did he step through the mirror and

come back to his own true love? Because that's what they are saying, Alan, isn't it, that Jamie and Peter were lovers when Peter disappeared, or, let's face it, was taken from him. At this point it feels uncannily like there is in fact someone behind the two-way mirror, God knows who or what, even. Did he step into his own shadow to be reunited with his perfect reflection? is what John St John really wants to ask him. And is the price we pay ash castles? is what John St John really wants to say. But John St John just sits there on the edge of the table like the best cop ever. Listen, Alan says, do you know anything about the magick of John Dee and Edward Kelley? I've been looking into it, John St John says. You have? Yes. And exactly what have you uncovered? Enochian, and the Towers, and the Transmitters, John St John says. Enochian is the original language of the angels, Alan says. It was transmitted to Dee and Kelley by angelic forces who promised them knowledge, wisdom, and ways beyond this fixed point in time, Alan Cardona says. I read that Kelley said an angel instructed him that they must swap their wives, Dee and Kelley, John St John says. Why would that be necessary? Because true initiation, Alan says, always involves some kind of transgressing of boundaries. Does he mention headless black birds in the sky at night? John St John asks him. At this point Liz executes an amateurish sketch of a silly headless bird at night. Alan says nothing. Let me tell you what I think happened, John St John says, and he leans forward, and he looms, in the way that makes him the best cop ever. Jamie entered the mirror and then came back to another life, with his true love, and another life again, is what I think, John St John says. There are infinite selves, endless lives to be lived, am I right? Alan says nothing. I have heard you called many things, Alan, he says, and one of them is The Disappearer. But perhaps, through your actions, you have stumbled across your true name. Perhaps you are, in truth, The Reanimator. At a signal Liz puts her pen and

paper to one side. Then: can you bring her back? John St
John asks Alan Cardona. Can you bring my angel back
to me?

THE SOCIETY OF THE SPECTACLE BY GUY DEBORD (DETROIT, 1968)

Original-but-worthless-'cause-it-is-all-covered-in-mould copy
of the first English translation of this incendiary tract (no
coincidence that it was first published in English in Detroit
in 1968) that meant so much to many of us, in the way it
woke us up from being mere spectators, mere consumers of
experience and culture, and urged, instead, participation in
the revolution of everyday life; form a band; paint a picture;
write a book; get lost; create a culture while you're at it.

What is it Gary Snyder says about Elders? About how there
are no real Elders any more, or maybe we're just not paying
attention any more because right after that he points out
that books are Elders, books are like entities, new entities,
speaking to us, if we can only listen, if we can only hear from
how far away they are speaking to us, then we would prick up
our ears; but where is the spectacle of a book speaking? That
was one of Guy Debord's biggest failings. As a writer, I prefer
Raoul Vaneigem.

PHOTOGRAPH OF SOME MAD OLD GEEZER WITH AN ALPACA SAT ON THE STEPS OF SOME CHURCH SOMEWHERE

Written on the back: 'remember, it doesn't get any better
than this'.

UNMADE BED

This is the most uncanny of them all, if you ask me, this
unmade bed. I said to Wee Humie, you didn't sleep in this
fucking unmade bed, did you? And he looked at me like I
was mental and said that he was ready to burn all of the soft
furnishings as soon as he got shot of the hippy shit, and so
I said to myself, there, is that Alan Cardona's final resting
place, or as close as we'll come, right there? Is that the shape
of his final body in the sheets? There's a last time we ever
lie down, it occurs to me, this is truly a mausoleum, it occurs
to me, and the bed sheets look like classical portraiture,
now, like baroque sculpture, now that it's over, the mound
of blankets upon blankets (he was a Taurus), I think of him
lying wrapped up in here in the winter, in the later years,
my God, it must have been brutal, but still special, and
memorable, hopefully, still like a final adventure, maybe, I
hope so, I hope so for Alan's sake, combing through this living
archive, this archive that he came to inhabit, on his own,
cut off from everything but the past, a centre around which
so many lives pivoted, but I've got to say, it stinks in here,
it really stinks in here, this place is a fucking dump to be
honest.

POSTCARD OF A SMILING STATUE

Pinned onto the wall behind the unmade bed, this implacable
head, with curls, forelocks, and hair hanging down on both
sides like a moptop, or is it a veil? The back reads: *statue de
kouros provenance théra* (detail).

POSTCARD OF DIANA DORS

Pinned onto the wall behind the unmade bed, The High
Priestess from the tarot deck, embodied.

KRISHNAMURTI BY CARLO SUARÈS (LES EDITIONS ADYAR, PARIS, 1933) (POOR)

Everyone was into this shit back then.

LARGE PILE OF PORN MAGS

I told you to forget those.

PHOTOGRAPH OF UNKNOWN CRASH PAD IN THE HOLEHILLS FLATS (CIRCA 1970?)

This is priceless. The pale sunlight through the windows. The plants in woven baskets hanging from the ceiling, the rugs on the walls. What's that on the stereo? It looks like John Fahey. You can smell the incense. Sandalwood. Dragon's Blood. There are pages from *Rolling Stone* and *International Times* pinned to the walls. A baby in nappies is crawling in the sunlight, in the light streaming through the windows it is motionless in joy. Honestly, that looks like a sitar behind the couch. The low table with candles and cacti and tarot cards, the cushions on the floor. Fags, and herbal tea. A poster that reads 'I Dig Your Body' and that has some psychedelic troll uprooting cadavers from a graveyard on it. Books. Something about Zen. Light.

DETECTIVE CONSTABLE JOHN MARIS ST JOHN CID BY CHRIS COLEMAN (MARKED-UP MANUSCRIPT)

John St John walks to Tollcross Library, where he has ordered some books in. He is reading in necromancy, and in demonology, which it occurs to him is another front in criminology. Repeatedly the books say that you must take dirt from the grave. Also, that you must burn something, that you must fumigate. He thinks of the ash castles. And how the grave is his father and his mother and his lover, combined. Who might resurrect, by accident? There is a tap on his shoulder and he turns with a start. It's Catherine, the treasurer of the Science Fiction Club. She has huge milk-bottle specs on. I see you are investigating those howlings, she says. And then, as if by way of explanation, I have to read books in the large print, she says, my eyesight is pitiful. Sure enough, she has a pile of those large-print yellow-jacket science-fiction novels that dominated libraries in the 1970s. You look nice in your glasses, Catherine says to him, and it is true that John St John needs reading glasses these days too, and it's also true that he is used to being spoken to like a little boy due to the hideous nature of his deformity. Thanks, he says. Well, she says, and she sort of stands there for a bit, if you're ever interested in science fiction you should feel free to join us some time, she says. I might do that, John St John says, and she says, okay, then, and he says, great, and she says, bye then, and John St John goes back to his reading, this time about a tree of blood inside a tree of crystal, and sure enough, here come the birds, the headless black birds are said to give books of illumination, he reads, and something catches at him, something he can't shake, a book, its reception, the times, something like that.

John St John listens to the radio at night and waits for the headless birds that never come. There is no mention of the nameless opponent of Maurice Yushenko, any more, he has been forgotten in a coma forever, at this point, and John St John imagines an internal night, still going on, somewhere impossible and with no one to comprehend it, and feels himself a prisoner in consciousness.

The tears come early, and easy, tonight, especially when someone sings 'The Skye Boat Song' on the radio, and he remembers his own father singing it to him, in turn, this boat, across never-ending seas, and with the rudder jammed, goddammit, he says to himself, and he gets up and he paces around the kitchen, and he hears something, something scratching, beneath the extension, in the foundation, somewhere, something moving fast, and scratching, several things now, and for some reason John St John writes it off, foxes, he says to himself, and he goes so far as to shrug, even, foxes getting up to no good down below, he says, that's all it is, he's too busy thinking about the birds, and expecting them, and he turns off the radio, and he switches off the light, and he heads upstairs for another fitful night of tears and lamentations, and all the while, these scratchings, and now these howlings, beneath things, are increasing, and speaking, in back of things, and that is when John St John stops being the best cop of all time.

PACKET OF SEEDS HAND-LABELLED 'LUPIN/FOXGLOVE'

And the words 'sticky willows' comes to mind, how these seeds transport me into a past where people gathered seeds and labelled them, and when sticky flowers stuck to your socks, in the summertime, or was it in the autumn. A culture that does not plant seeds, well, there is something about that, that tipping over into consumption from out of begetting that is the true story of the 1960s, and the hippies, which everyone knows lasted till about 1975 (the sixties).

CATERPILLAR #14 (JANUARY 1971, FRONT COVER BY WALLACE BERMAN, 'TOPANGA SEED') (VG+)

HALF-EATEN PACKET OF WEETABIX

Minging.

HALF-EMPTY BOTTLE OF VOSENE

There was somebody at every school I went to in Airdrie
who was supposed to have got their cock stuck in a bottle of
Vosene while having a wank and had to go to the Accident
& Emergency to get it removed. That guy's a Vosene, they
would say, and point him out, solemn, like that. So, the big
question is, was Alan Cardona a Vosene? We'll never know,
now. But you've got to admit, it's suspect.

RED-AND-WHITE OLD GOLF UMBRELLA

Wasn't it Blake's pal, William Hayley, who kept falling from
horses onto his umbrella?

MOTH-EATEN BLUE-AND-WHITE BUDDHIST ROBE

Alan Cardona's father was a practising Zen Buddhist. In
Holehills, he led the way. He was the first head ever to move
into the flats, well before anyone knew what a head, never
mind a Freak, never mind a Buddhist, was. People would
yell at him in the street, fucking Hare Krishna, kids would
yell. At school, kids would tease Alan about his dad being a
chinky. But then one time a beloved dog that belonged to a
family that lived in the block next door was hit by a car and
Fred (Alan's dad) had kneeled over it and performed some
kind of rite of peace or something, and they were so moved,
the family, when they saw it, this old guy with a bush of
prematurely silver hair and a great grey beard, stroking the
head of this dying dog while chanting some kind of mantra
in the middle of Chapel Street, that the family asked him to

perform a Zen funeral service for it, for Ringo, the dog, and he performed this ceremony, in full Zen regalia, in the back courts, for Ringo, and there were people sat out there on deckchairs, and children crammed into the open windows, and people brought picnics and drank beer and smoked cigarettes while Fred chanted mantras over the grave of this dead dog, Ringo, all the while steaming drunk, it has to be said, Fred was a drinker and he was rat-arsed, eyewitnesses report, so that at the climax he danced around the grave in a circle with a can of McEwan's Export balanced on his head while playing some mad Tibetan bullroarer, in full Zen regalia, and the story is that he never spilt a single drop, and everyone agreed it was the most Zen thing anyone had ever seen, and soon he was burying all the pets in the area.

ISSUE OF GERMAN ART MAG *PROTO*

Some German art rag came all the way over to Airdrie to review the anti-Vietnam protest gig at Airdrie Town Hall, this guy, Gerhard Gabler. 'Here, are new concepts of light, and painting. Using fluids and slides and dyes, projected onto the back wall of the hall, I almost said the soul, so intense was the performance, so new, that the forms and the strange geometries felt like entities, struggling to birth, like the pain of a new language, coming into existence. Time is erased, the music is overwhelming, the visuals are pulsing, around you people are dancing, some spinning slowly in a circle, some freaking out, one guy wearing a ponytail and a pair of Tibetan pyjamas jumping up and down on the spot like he might up-anchor and float off, in rapture, the light show was moving, emotional, inexplicably so, those uncanny resonances of birth, all of that struggling cosmos, there is a concomitant blurring of inside and out, so that at points it felt like everything was the contents of your head, or crazier still, that really you had no head at all. Afterwards, on the walk home, it was the exact same thing with the night sky.'

DETECTIVE CONSTABLE JOHN MARIS ST JOHN CID BY CHRIS COLEMAN (MARKED-UP MANUSCRIPT)

Someone has made an official complaint about Detective Constable John Maris St John CID. It's a historical complaint. John St John is accused of running a racket. By his angel Carol's ex-husband, who is a hippy bastard, these days, and a pox on his life, if he's honest, and who was now bringing up Carol's kids, against their will, against his will, John St John's steel will, that is, John St John who had petitioned to get custody of the children after Carol died, and who had made life for these hippies a living nightmare, let's be honest, back then, and of course what chance did he have against the biological father, and of course he made threats, invented reasons to bust them, spread rumours of abusive and unsanitary conditions, why did he do that? He can no longer recognise the self that did that, he was vicious, monomaniacal, this same self that ran a racket back then, it's true. And of course he involved Carol, he felt like they were romantic outlaws with their backs to the wall and no one to trust but each other like in a crazy love pact. And now her husband had evidence and was seeking revenge.

John St John takes a book from his bookshelf. He has about five books at home, two of which are word search compendiums, as well as a set of encyclopaedias. He opens a page of the encyclopaedia at random. They are talking about how maybe gods were actually ancient spacemen who visited humankind at the dawn of their great adventure to sort of wish them luck and inspire some art and reverence in them. No. Now they are talking about fish raining down from the skies. What kind of encyclopaedia is this? Now they are talking about spontaneous human combustion aka SHC.

John St John is poring over a proposed list of factors common to the majority of SHC cases.

1. Alcoholism/drug abuse.
2. Marginalised lives.
3. Bodies tend to have to be lit externally from something, at first, at least, rather than igniting internally.
4. The hands and feet are often preserved.
5. The burning body usually doesn't do much damage to any combustible surroundings.
6. Stinky ashes, a very particular stinky; John St John reads it again.
7. The presence of mirrors in the room.

This isn't helping.

CATALOGUE FOR EXHIBITION OF PAINTINGS BY CASSIE

The first time I ever made love I will never forget it. I mean, I had had sex, I had fucked my share of women, and I thought I had made love to many of them along the way. But you know it when it happens, and suddenly, there it is: you're making love. I can only compare it to a feeling like where all of the boundaries between yourself and the beloved come down, all the self-consciousness, all of the intricacies of performance and technique, disappear, and there is your perfect other, held, by the waist, tender, and horny, delicate kisses on the cheek, your make-up smeared, the first time I ever made love was with Cassie, in her flat, in Airdrie, and it is still one of the most sacred nights of my life.

Afterwards I lay in the bath, in the candlelight, while she sat on the can and read the first of Rilke's *Duino Elegies* to me, in her beautiful American accent. Then she climbed into the bath next to me and urinated, silently, into the water. It is still the most romantic thing that anyone has ever done for me.

'Cassie is a painter of visionary depth and power, drawing on occult relationships between colour and certain ratios of frequency in order to map the shadowed borderlands of the noumenal world. Cassie grew up in an art commune in West Virginia run by Theosophists. Her first exhibition, The Burning World, was hosted in an abandoned shack high in the Appalachian Mountains where every window was framed as in a painting. She was artist in residence, and slept there, and when anyone would come to visit, she would sing a version of a romantic hillbilly ballad through a tiny speaker. The exhibition, which ran for three weeks, attracted a single visitor, her mother, who was making sure she had enough to eat. Cassie declared the action a success. But soon she moved into painting. Cassie takes Charles Olson's rendering of "primitive" as "primary", as "essential". There is an intricacy to her technique, an architectural quality, even as she uses basic shapes and geometries, crudely rendered. Relationship of visual elements is key. The shapes are not so much symbols as stresses and strains, elements of energy, and force. The various elements seem to be partaking of a kind of *conference of becoming*, as such they feel like entity, like power. In the mid-1960s Cassie lived in a disused windmill in Sussex, before moving to Airdrie in a life-experiment that is still on-going. This is the first retrospective of her work.'

ORIGINAL MOTH-EATEN HANDMADE AFGHAN SUEDE COAT WITH YELLOW-AND-WHITE EMBROIDERY

In Afghanistan again. With Suzy. What I hear is that Suzy is kidnapped. She had been attracting a lot of attention; blonde, tall, dressing like a sexually liberated aristocrat in the middle of all this desert. They make it to Kandahar, there's some poet they have arranged to meet there, some guy out visiting his guru who lived in a cave outside the city. They hole up in a ratty apartment in a rundown area. They try to make connections. Coats, rugs, but all anyone wants to talk about is guns, or drugs. They make a connection. Alan smokes heroin for the first time and is blown away by it. Him and Suzy both. They develop a habit. Now they're talking about smuggling heroin back. In the marketplace there are catcalls and leers and much ball-grabbing from passers-by as Suzy makes her way through the crowd in a mini-dress, a floppy hat and oversized sunglasses. Some men flash cash as if Suzy was for sale. Others are more aggressive. Their neighbours are watching them through a crack in their door. At night, there are footsteps and whispered voices in the stairwell. One night there's a shadow on the fire escape. In the morning there is a dead bat pinned to their door by its wings. They hook up with the poet, who was apparently a famous Greek poet, translated in English here and there, and he introduces them to this kind of expat cell of poets and artists, who all meet at this café, which is really a secret drinking den, and they get rat-arsed and smoke heroin together and talk about the nature of consciousness as a perfect pearl – this is Kandahar, 1969 – and it turns out that one of the guys, maybe not a poet, but a would-be bohemian, I guess, one of these guys had actually sold his wife, to some Bedouins, and she wasn't unwilling, these Bedouins had offered him good money for his girl, and assured him that she would be treated well, that she was, in fact, a rare jewel, that was the phrase

that struck Alan, that rare jewel companion, and, yeah, this
guy's girl had headed off into the desert with these madmen
never to be seen again, and, as he said, not unwillingly.

Someone ran a printing press in the rear, strictly samizdat,
and they were issuing these weirdo poetry and graphic
art zines, like with like black psychedelic imagery, and
concrete poetry, and journal extracts while on heroin in the
mountains, etc., real frontier-of-consciousness stuff. Then
one day this Greek poet guy asks Alan if he would like to
accompany him on his pilgrimage to the cave of his guru. No
chicks allowed, he adds. Okay, so as Suzy stays home, and
smokes heroin, and falls asleep on the bed, most probably,
but who knows. Who knows. Alan and this guy, this Greek
poet guy, who has barely been translated at all, now that I
look into it, how did he ever come across this footnote, but by
now they are crossing this desert, heading for this skull, this
rock formation shaped like a skull in whose left eye this guy's
guru was and probably still is right at this moment pointing
his cock to galactic zero, and they climb up, and present
themselves to this guru, who acted like he was blind, who
looked like he was blind, and who immediately put his hand
out in front of him and said, no, no, no what, no, no blotting
out the light, he said, and he had them move, out of the light,
even though he was blind he was receiving the light, which
was the first lesson right there, Alan reckoned, and then he
said, this guru in a cave, he asked them, did you bring me
treats, and when they said, yeah, they brought like fruit and
nuts and incense, the guru sort of sighed and said, I'm pining
away up here, you think I couldn't murder a Curlywurly,
and Alan said it was like total enlightenment, this guy was
so real, but then he said, directed to Alan, this time, are you
in mourning, he said, did someone die, he said, what do you
mean, Alan said, I mean, he said, what's all that weight,
this blind guru said, at which exact moment, it is possible

to speculate, Suzy's unconscious form was even then being spirited from the apartment, and carried down the fire escape by parties unknown.

EDDIE COCHRAN DOUBLE LP ON UNITED ARTISTS (POOR)

Eddie Cochran died in a car crash in England in 1960. Gene Vincent was injured in the same crash, as was Cochran's girlfriend, the songwriter Sharon Sheeley. In those days the streetlights in England went out at midnight. The story is that the driver had been blinded by a light and had taken a turn down the wrong way on a motorway. This is what Teddy Ohm told me. While trying to turn back around he had lost control and hit a lamppost, throwing Cochran through the back of the car and out, onto the road, alongside his guitar. And at that exact moment, the lights went out. Dave Dee, who would soon be a dead pop star himself, was working as a policeman back then, and was first on the scene. There were bodies scattered around in the darkness. The light had gone out, he confirmed. Dave took Cochran's guitar back to the station, Teddy said, and taught himself how to play.

Teddy claimed that Eddie Cochran was a psychedelic avatar. Like the first stirring of psychedelic energy was the life, and death, of Eddie Cochran, who sang 'C'mon Everybody' and 'Somethin' Else'. What was a psychedelic sensibility? An experimenting with consciousness. An attempt at attention. A relationship to light. Light. L.V.X.

LETTERS OF THE ALPHABET

Okay, so there are letters of the alphabet in this caravan, in books, in letters, in magazines, on the walls, I'm using them to describe it, even; the letters are here. Which brings me to Bobby Barton aka 'AB'. He wrote a book under the pseudonym 'AB' called *Telegraph Material Universe*. Only no one ever read it. Although he did perform it in public, occasionally, in the late sixties, most famously, most notoriously, for Lanarkshire heads, was the time he read this mad book aloud at the Old Dragon Underground Anti-Vietnam War Protest at Airdrie Town Hall, he was on the bill, there were a bunch of poets and writers appearing during the day, and he read this book only he read it out letter by letter h e s p e l l e d i t o u t l i k e t h i s, in individual letters, so that it was impossible to follow, only as some kind of Morse code, some kind of semaphoring, from this desolate place in his heart, it occurs to me, who writes a whole book only to spell it out, and the thing was he said he would never allow anyone to read it or have it published because to him that was the ultimate cop-out, selling out, reconciling, making sense. Sovereign, he called it, remaining sovereign, was the thing, he would insist. But a tape exists, a reel-to-reel that was recorded by an amateur soundman, and there are a few minutes of him reading and I transcribed a bit:

i n t o t h e r e a l m s a c r e d e m o n s t r a t i o n t o l o g i c a l l o g o r h y t h m o l e c u l e n t o p i c t o r i a l i b e r a t e d o n o m a t o l o g i s t e l e g r a p h m a t e r i a l u n i v e r s e

And no one ever got to read it. And then what I heard was that he fell in love with Fleur Mayberry and when she didn't reciprocate, he killed himself. Overthrown, just like that.

HAND-WRITTEN CASSETTE: *EDDIE COCHRAN LIVE AT TOWN HALL PARTY 1959*

SIDE A

'Town Hall Party Intro'
'C'mon Everybody'
'Have I Told You Lately That I Love You?'
'Don't Blame It on Me'
'Summertime Blues (Encore)'
'Johnny Bond Interviews Eddie Cochran'

SIDE B

'Town Hall Party Intro'
'School Days'
'Be Honest with Me'
'Money Honey'
'C'mon Everybody'

HALF-SMOKED FAG PACKET OF 20 REGAL SMALL

Same brand that Cassie smoked.

J.D. BLACKFOOT, 'WHO'S NUTS ALFRED'/'EPITAPH FOR A HEAD', ORIGINAL 7-INCH 1969 (PHILIPS 40625) (NM)

This is rare as hell. Looks almost Unplayed. One of the great psychedelic guitar bombs.

FOLD-OUT MAP OF AIRDRIE AND ITS SURROUNDINGS (1968)

There are asterisks across the map at certain points, joined
by lines, so that they intersect in the shape of a five-pointed
star. There was this idea; see where you are, and what you
can do there. Again, it was Gary Snyder who came up with
it, you know, don't hitch-hike across America, don't drop out
in Woodstock, think local, think of the specifics of the ecology
you live in, come to name its trees and birds, come to know
its wildlife, but not just that, its stone, its geological history,
its wild-man roots, and one sure way was by working magick
on it, work magick on it, say the magick word and point
to it, draw the cardinal points around it, and find out that
where you are was the centre of the world all along. Which is
exactly what we were up to in these towns and villages of the
Monklands in the 1960s.

OLD BUCKET FILLED WITH RUSTED TROWELS
AND FORKS

Ah but this is sad, though. All that remains of that mad
experiment in living that the Calderbank Allotments
represented, once. This is where Alan lived, after he left the
Holehills flats, he lived in a hut that some old duffer had built
in the first summer after the Great War, and then in this very
caravan, once they were all demolished, on this allotment
that was privately owned, and so there was no council red
tape, and so no such thing as planning permission, back then,
so that a bunch of hobos moved in and just began living there
full-time, and growing their own veg – which hippies would
sell door-to-door in Calderbank – they were welcomed, back
then, the working class in these Lanarkshire villages hadn't
yet become the small-minded, hate-filled, bigoted alcoholics
they are now and back then there was basically an annexe of

Woodstock down behind the garages, the huts were works of art, all built from salvage, some with multiple storeys and tall decks built up in the sun, and little hobbit huts, and there were nights where they would build bonfires outside, the hippies, and people would sit around and drink wine all night and play hand-drums as the sun came up, and if you can see for miles, then right there, on the deck, behind the guy with the acoustic guitar, and that guy using an apple as a bong, you might make out the long-ago silhouette of me and Cassie, on the night of our first date, singing 'The More I See You' by Chris Montez and 'Wichita Lineman' by Glen Campbell, all of us, singing there, together.

PHOTOGRAPH OF CASSIE

Okay so I snuck this in here so as you could see how beautiful she was. Do you know how much I loved this girl? Her blonde hair and her dark eyes, people said she looked like a blonde Grace Slick, or sometimes France Gall, the little diamond stud in her nose, a little wild gypsy vibe, I had never seen that before. I had gone to see her exhibition, in Airdrie Arts Centre, there had been no one there but me, and her, her sat behind this giant lectern for some reason, so that it was like approaching some kind of goddess in an Egyptian court, and me clanging around in this empty, echoing room, there was no carpet on the floor and every footstep was a clang, so that I was standing for inordinately long periods of time in front of these amazing paintings, these force fields, it seemed to me, that's exactly what they were like, circuits, charged points, transmitters, and it was like the final circuit point was you, and in the seeing of it, you set it off, I'm thinking all of these mad thoughts and hoping for my feet not to clang, when she gets up, Cassie, and announces to no one but me and the room, fuck this, I'm out of here, she announces, and I couldn't suppress a laugh, and she laughed too and she said, know anywhere I can get high, and I said, I know exactly the place, it's a hippy encampment just outside Calderbank called Gethsemane.

LITTLE WRAP OF SPEED IT LOOKS LIKE ON THE FLOOR THERE

I'm having that, up the hooter, for old times' sake, etc., though for me it's new times' sake, I'm an old bugger, and I didn't get into it all until my own life fell apart and I lost everything I ever was.

I had the full deal, the whole suburban 1960s dream, living in a new estate, up near Caldervale, my wife was a police officer, my mother had talked me into marrying her, because, I see now, I think now, anyway, that she saw something in me, something truthful in me, something wild and irrepressible in me, something that she couldn't bear, and she wanted to kill it dead, because our family was so fearful, so distrusting, of the depths of their own selves, that their lives were prison sentences or not at all, and so I had got married, against my deep-down better judgement, it's true, did I love her, I feel as if I pitied her, which is the worst thing, her disfigurement, I pitied it, I admired her fortitude, her bravery, I convinced myself she had a beautiful soul, a beautiful spirit, and that's what I was marrying, an angel, what did I know, what example did I have of happiness in my life, happiness was something furtive, something that happened behind the back of your family, out of necessity and shame, and she was a policewoman, and she was conscientious, and she did her job well, apart from one time when she came home with a wad of banknotes down her tights.

I thought she was acting suspiciously and then I caught her
in the mirror of the wardrobe, through the door, taking this
wad of notes out of her tights and hiding them in one of her
drawers. Look, we had two kids by this point, my mum would
look after them. I had a decent job working for a painting
and decorating firm. I don't know why I didn't push it, just
ask her straight out, I just knew that secrets were the things
that happened in back of families, it's just, so okay, I find out
that she is having an affair with this detective constable, this
crooked constable, who is running some kind of racket, some
kind of protection thing, he was rolling criminals, basically,
and maybe that was truly all they fucking deserved, who
knows, but anyway Carol started changing, it was like
Bonnie and Clyde, they thought they were a romantic pair of
gangsters, mad enforcers, and then one night I come home
and she's in her dressing gown on the couch and he is fully
clothed, and he said he just dropped her off, that's what he
said to me, I just dropped Carol off, he said, and he was a
giant, and he had a deformity, a terrible facial deformity, it
was awful, like he was the mirror image of Carol, like they
were made in each other's image, and he just bore down on
me and said, I just dropped your wife off for you, he said, *for
you*, he said, like he was doing me a favour, stepping up to
the plate when I was unable, and the thing was, Carol was
clearly enjoying it, she couldn't help but grin on the couch
when he said that, this giant grotesque constable, and then
he made a joke about our shelving, we had just bought a new
modular shelving unit for the home-entertainment system
and he pointed to it and he said, it makes it much easier to
get it up, doesn't it, he said, as he passed by, at least I think
that's what he said, and Carol giggled, but rather than say
excuse me but what the fuck did you just say, I said, yeah,
it does, mate, it does, and I opened the door and let him out
and my wife said, I'm knackered, I'm off to bed, and I had no
friends outside of my rotten family, at this point in my life,

and didn't know what to do or how to start again, and that's
when I started hanging about Da Capo, the record shop in
town, and met this guy Tom Paterson, who's dead now, and
bought grass from Tobias and listened to *Easter Everywhere*
and the rest is history.

PLASTIC BAG FOR DA CAPO RECORDS ON SOUTH BRIDGE STREET, AIRDRIE

The story with Da Capo Records was that the guys that ran it
were both major Arthur Lee heads and named the shop after
the second Love album, which came out in 1966, but then the
very next year when Love released *Forever Changes* – and
The Beatles released *Sgt. Pepper's* – there was a schism,
with Simon announcing it was the end of true rock 'n' roll
and the beginning of some kind of pseudo-classical baroque
pop (he would compare the lyrics of Bobby Darin's 'Splish
Splash'/'Judy Don't Be Moody' to the lyrics of John Lennon
and roll his eyes at 'newspaper taxis appear on the shore')
while Brian saw it as the future, a new music, a playful
cultural moment that exploded the rock/roll blueprint to
take in influences from all over, and there was a falling-out,
with the result that they split the shop in two, right down
the middle, and each had their own stock and they had their
checkout desks facing each other, on either side of the shop,
like it was a grudge match, and of course Simon had a cut-off
date of 1966, he only stocked 'spiritually pure' rock 'n' roll
released before 1967 while Brian said fuck it, in that case
I will only stock new music post-'66. Can you imagine an
equivalent moment of cultural trust and gravity today? To
bet it all, on the moment, in complete faith? Of course the
true heads shopped on both sides of the shop, we were all into
our British-invasion shit, especially The Who, The Kinks, The
Zombies, The Troggs and Small Faces, and of course blues

and country and rockabilly and soul, but we needed the new
Beefheart album, the new Quicksilver Messenger Service, the
new Floyd, the new Dead, the first United States of America
LP, shit like Coltrane, Pharaoh Sanders, ESP-Disk. Of
course, people wouldn't realise it was two separate shops with
two separate tills and amateurs would go up to the counter
with vinyl from both sides and Simon would be casting
out every second record and rolling his eyes and saying,
his, his, his, while slamming them down on the counter.
Simon famously coined the term 'the doughnut effect' while
complaining to Teddy Ohm about the kind of people who buy
alla these obscure garage and psych sides while not even
having core works by people like The Kinks and The Stones
and The Who. To which Teddy famously responded, you are
a fucking doughnut, which supposedly got him banned from
the shop, but Simon was too scared to enforce it, so he just
continued to serve him through gritted teeth regardless.
They finally packed it in in the early 2000s, when Brian had
to admit there was truly no longer any present, or future,
worth championing, and Simon felt vindicated that his dire
prediction of the way things were headed back in 1967 had
been proved right all along. The only modern bands the two
ever agreed on were The Monarchs of the Night Time and
The Modern Lovers.

CUTTING THROUGH SPIRITUAL MATERIALISM BY CHÖGYAM TRUNGPA

Classic.

DETECTIVE CONSTABLE JOHN MARIS ST JOHN CID BY CHRIS COLEMAN (MARKED-UP MANUSCRIPT)

A photograph has been received, or rather, a photograph of a photograph has been received. It is a photograph of a photograph of Carol pulling her dress up to reveal envelopes stuffed with money down her black tights. Her pale skin seems so terribly pale as it overflows the band of her tights. Her tender face is obscured by her black dress over her head. I remember that underwear, John St John thinks to himself. I stuffed those envelopes down there myself, he marvels.

After a night of bright tears and soft lamentations, John St John leaves the house early on his bicycle but instead of turning right, towards the CID, he turns left, and cycles up to Barlanark and takes the Edinburgh Road to Bargeddie – the only people up at this hour are the poor and the simple-minded – up through Coatdyke to Whinhall, he cycles along Mavisbank Street in the gloomy early-morning light, and it is just like Christmas, like a miserable Christmas, out here, this morning.

John St John gets off his bike and leans it on a fence. Then he stands there facing number 79, at the end of the driveway he stands there, and he waits.

How long has he been standing there motionless like an awful terror at this point? But someone is coming to the door. It is his angel Carol's unnamed ex-husband. Why is he unnamed? Because he has become the opponent. The opponent glances up, and is startled, who wouldn't be, by John St John's stark presence there, his stark, ugly, terrifying presence there, at the end of the driveway, stood there, in a street in Whinhall, at this time of the morning, on the most miserable Christmas day the mind could draw up, like a terror.

Hello there, John St John says, and he waves at the opponent in an exaggerated fashion. The unnamed opponent looks worried. Hi, he says, and he makes speed to get into his car. Now he's fumbling with the lock. While John St John is just standing there. I received your photograph, John St John says to him, calmly. However, it is not our dear departed Carol who is on trial here. It is you and I, he says. But already the unnamed opponent is opening the door of the car. I loved her when you were incapable of it, John St John announces.

I knew you would be here, John St John continues, even as the car door is slammed shut and the unnamed ex-husband is reversing out of the driveway. I knew I would find you at your mother's, John St John says, and he sneers at him. Does she look after the children you are also incapable of loving? John St John mocks him, as he speeds off in his car. He thinks he sees the face of a woman in the window, the mother, perhaps, but it disappears in a flash. And John St John is stood there, in the now-silent street, stood there staring at this house in this silence, this house of his unnamed opponent's mother, and he is mocking, and cruel, over what he perceives as this clown's failure to grow up, when really, it is just as impossible to imagine John St John bringing up children as it is to imagine some hopeless Lanarkshire mummy's boy hippy bastard doing the same.

Q.B.L. OR THE BRIDE'S RECEPTION, BEING A SHORT CABALISTIC TREATISE ON THE NATURE AND USE OF THE TREE OF LIFE WITH A BRIEF INTRODUCTION AND A LENGTHY APPENDIX BY FRATER ACHAD, DEDICATED UNTO THE 'ADMIRABLE OR HIDDEN INTELLIGENCE' WHICH IS IN ALL (LIMITED EDITION

There is a handwritten letter inside. It is from the poet
Jack Hirschman, who was then living at 21 Quarterdeck,
Venice, Calif. to the poet/actor Alan Marlowe – then husband
of Diane di Prima – living at 1915 Oak St, San Francisco,
California. The postmark is torn but it is November 1968:

Dear Alan, You folks are welcome here, room to spare
with meself leaving on the 11th (three readings in
London from *BLACK ALEPHS* to announce the new
regime of death and visit graveside of Master Willy for
later parch-ment kabbalas). Ruth (*!?*) is working days
as you know so regrets not being able to pick you up at
the airport, though I figure you're coming in by car??
At any rate the front door will be closed, so come down
the left side of house and in the back entrance. Ruth
(*!?*) happens to be off from work the 12th so if you
want to check out matters I'd suggest you call. At 392-
2734. okay. Happy to hear of the studied good works.
I am leaving on my desk a copy of *QBL, The Bride's
Reception*. It is a very rare manuscript, and I know
you will not be able to read it during your stay, and it
can't go back up with you just now, but I hope the two,
four, eight and sixtyfour of you have a chance to look
at it anyway. It is one of two books (The other is called
The Anatomy of the Body of God) written by a disciple
of Crowley in Chicago and given to Malcolm Lowry in
Canada when he was writ-ing the Volcano. His widow,
who lives here, passed them to me some years ago. The
other was lost in shuffles, but I mean to get a xeroxed
copy of it one day soon again. Okay. Be well here.
Luv
Jack

PS. Election nearly over/new occasions for midnight gilguls.

PPS. Harry Norse, poet returned from Europe, is here in Venice – 15 Paloma, 392-7544. Bklyn!

OLD YURT ROLLED UP WITH WOODEN POLES AND TIED WITH ROPE

Okay, a tent, inside a yurt, inside a caravan, what kind of Russian-doll scene is this? My guess is that this is the yurt that they held feasts in at Gethsemane. Alan was a good cook, so was Teddy, and Effie, well ahead of the curve, and of course they were growing their own vegetables up there, kale, broccoli, potatoes, of course, broad beans, French beans, asparagus, there was this mad wild asparagus patch, sunflowers, quince, they had a fucking quince tree on the go back then, Effie had gathered seeds from the quinces that used to grow all around the Bowling Basin, we would often cycle all the way there, in the autumn, all the way across Glasgow just to gather fruits to make jam with, plus plums, all sorts of berries, garlic, onions, broccoli, did I say broccoli, courgettes, listen, there were no mobile phones, fewer cars, and no electricity, only the occasional wireless blasting out, the kids tearing across the fields on motorbikes on the other side of the valley the only sound in the shimmering heat, the distant sound of screams and laughter echoing across the valley, and they would throw huge dinners in this yurt round the back of Alan's cabin, this old military yurt, and with candles, and with a handwritten menu, Alan had all these old blank French menus that he found on his travels, and he would handwrite the courses, and each course was preceded by a toast and the reciting of a poem of gratitude, and the night we were there, the night I brought Cassie there, one of the hippies stood up and read the love letters of Dylan Thomas to Caitlin, in the spring of 1950, I had never heard them before, wow: my love, my love, my love, I miss you, my love, (I love you), Caitlin, Cassie, my love, was how they went, and there was wine, and there was cider, everyone was determined not to drink beer, it didn't seem sacramental enough, and this cider was absolutely mental – stank like pig piss and trippy as hell – so that afterwards everyone went out on the deck and someone had a telescope and we took it in turns to lie on our backs and gaze up and into – I couldn't believe you could do that – the craters on the moon. The first time I saw inside a crater on the moon was on my first date with Cassie, what kind of Russian-doll scene is this?

THE GREAT BEAST: THE LIFE OF ALEISTER CROWLEY BY JOHN SYMONDS (RIDER 1951) (G+)

This is the exact edition my wife brought up during our custody battle. She claimed that I was practising 'black magic' and that she was concerned for the safety of our children. Exhibit fucking A.

A FEATHER

A single black feather.

Alan comes back from this trip to this guru in this mountain outside Kandahar that is shaped like a skull and he finds that Suzy is gone, all except for a black feather, on the fire escape he finds a single black feather, and isn't there some group that worships a black bird and a sacred fire in the desert, and so Alan gets it into his head that Suzy has been kidnapped by some heretical gnostic sect that worships Shaitan, and so he starts asking around, about apostates, about heretics, where are these fuckers hiding out, he says, they've got my girlfriend, he says, these peacock-fuckers, these pagan retards, and soon people are coming to him, I hate infidels, they're saying, I despise heretics, I spit on their mother, they say, and soon there's a story about a community living in the desert who prostrate themselves in front of some kind of bird god and Alan is putting a party together to raid them, goaded on by these mad Afghan fundamentalists, who are spoiling for a massacre, or at least a wholesale assault, on these creeps in the mountains, these creeps that I fucking spit on, they're saying, they have your woman, brother, they're saying, and they're feeding Alan smack and that mad mountain hash, so that he's in a permanent fever, these fuckers, they're saying, they will have raped her many times by now, they're adding, they will probably have her fornicate with birds, they're adding, falcons, they're saying, she will be making love with falcons, against her will, and where do you think they put their talons, they're adding, and what about their beaks, they are razor-sharp, my friend, they are saying, all these friends now, all these brothers.

FLYER FOR A BENEFIT CONCERT TO SUPPORT THE BUSTING OF THE WAR WOUND BOOKSHOP

The War Wound got busted for selling Fleur Mayberry's *My Menses*, even though it was bullshit. They were looking for an excuse to shut down the shop because education is a dangerous thing in working-class towns, especially an alternative education, so they charged in and seized all of their stock, everything, all the paperbacks and incense and posters and chapbooks, everything, on the basis that they were stocking obscene material. This was a turning point, in the militancy of the hippies, locally, and the beginning of the spiral, really, in so many ways.

The Old Dragon Underground presents A War Wound Benefit. Light Show: Industry of Magic & Light. Sound Show: Butler & Ohm. Poets: Fleur Mayberry, Ian Cunningham, Effie Darrow, AB. Artist in Residence: Cassie. Live music: Kommandos of Daath, The Hungry Birds, Mammüt & Gryphon. 7 p.m. till late. The Operative Lodge of Airdrie 203, Clark Street, Airdrie.

HANDBILL FOR THE WAR WOUND BOOKSHOP, CURRENT BOOKS FOR SALE

Make all cheques payable to Bob Warwick, 28 Anderson Street, Airdrie, ML6 0AA.

1. George Dowden. *Because I Am Tired of the Night*, 1966, Sussex. Signed, inscribed copy of book of poems from this major UK head with connections to *Poetmeat*/Dave Cunliffe/Tina Morris et al. 5.00
2. David Meltzer. *Tree #1*, 1970, San Francisco. New journal edited by Meltzer, author of *Yesod*, with a heavy kabbalistic focus plus avant-garde, ethnopoetics; features Hirschman, Grossinger, Zukofsky, Brakhage, Weiners, Kelley, Herms, Eshleman and Blake (From the Note-Book). 2.00
3. Roxie Powell. *Dreams of Straw*, 1963, San Francisco, Auerhahn Press. First edition, letterpressed by Dave Haselwood and Charles Plymell, edition of 250 copies, rare talismanic edition of this weirdo fringe poet's best work, later issued by Cherry Valley Editions. 12.50
4. Clyde Bayswater. *Jokes and Their Relation to the Walking Dead*, 1969, Glasgow, Barricades Press. Signed, inscribed ('A Spare Key to the Humours

of the Underground') copy of book of poems and street photography, documenting Bayswater's street happenings in Glasgow in the mid-1960s. 3.00

5. Steve Richmond. *Hitler Painted Roses*, 1966, Santa Monica, Earth Books. First edition, signed, now-classic collection, extensive foreword by friend Charles Bukowski. 6.50

6. Ian Cunningham. *Atlas-Zeus*, 1969, Coatbridge, Darkside Books. Signed, numbered edition of fifty copies, black psychedelic/mindfuck prose/poetry from this local imprint. 1.00

7. Christopher Perret. *Memorial Volume 1930–1965*, 1966, Switzerland, Poésie vivante. Posthumous collection of this promising artist/poet/bohemian's prose, journals, paintings, photography, etc., who died at the age of thirty-five in Deià, on the island of Mallorca, in 1965. 2.50

8. Fleur Mayberry. *My Menses*, 1969, Coatbridge, Darkside Books. Signed, numbered edition of fifty copies, love/sex poetry and menstrual paintings. 1.00

9. Arthur Bush. *Aztec Jim Morrison (for Alexander Calder)*, 1970. Coatbridge, Darkside Books. Sculptural prose, poetry and line drawings from this Carbeth-based poet. Silkscreened covers, hand-numbered edition of sixty-nine copies. 1.00

LETTER TO BOB WARWICK OF THE WAR WOUND BOOKSHOP FROM THE POET GEORGE DOWDEN

George Dowden
11B Adelaide Crescent
(Entrance Holland Road)
HOVE, Sussex BN3 2JE
England

Midear Bob

Well, it's a relief to know that my books arrived and that you're okay. Thanks for letter and cheque. I'll send 12 more copies of next book on your standing order, when it is ready in a few months – unless I hear differently from you. Should sell for about two pounds. I'll still give you 50% off – for, uh, paying right away!

Your letter was good. Excuse me for doubting you but xxxx I had to consider all possibilities. I am delighted to hear that you feel my presence in the silence there. Yes, my yoga is getting better and better and lots of people are responding to it. I seem right on schedule for the Self-realisation predicted for me by Muktananda's astrologer. I may become a swami – in any case I'll open a centre and serve many more people at that time, if not before. I have come out of my 'cave yogi' situation somewhat in the past two weeks – since meeting an extraordinary young girl, art student who paints the mystic reality in trees very well. She says I saved her life – and she has done me a lot of good. We meditate together andx she has already had several meaningful experiences and looks like being a most ripe candidate for Siddha Yoga. It's great joy to xxxx serve her and to have her and be with her. Even if I lost her tomorrow, so much good has been done I'll never lose her. She was certainly sent to me by Muktananda as I was sent to her. We've been great catalysts to each other.

Okay, I can dig what you say about your reactions not being important, about our relationship being on a level beyond thoughts and actions. Good. Let it be pure spirit. Whatever is good or bad in ISIS, by the way, is equal – it was all part of my consciousness at the time, and that is what I wanted to get down, and I accepted the extreme difficulty and challenge of writing under

LSD and ;et most of what I wriote stand without
revision, a record of what the Acid and smoke was
expressing through me, a record of my personal, more
than aesthetic, experience.

My head is, thankfully, into Oneness more and
more now – the ultimate yogic awareness – and my
poems are expressing manifestations of that. The
enclosed is one expression of that Oneness. It's just
two months old. I have written three more poems since
then. You may not know all the Sanskrit words, but
you'll get the idea and the feeling. I know my audience
– yogic seekers, especially yogic seekers following
Muktananda Guru – and my poems are reaching them
(if no one else) these days. Whenever one appears in
an Ashram publication, I'm guaranteed about 30,000
readers – can't complain! 'Bahut schcha,' I might say,
means 'very good' – and PRANAM is of course a bow.

Yes, do send your new catalogue!

Bob, I feel your love and being and I respond to that.
I want you to know that you have a place in my heart
and I have a place in yours. Yes. My 'return to India' is
happening all the time – as Muktananda is my India
and I'm coming to him more and more in my heart. He
may be starting next world tour soon, and I may join
him.

Keep well, keep silent joy going. You're too silent
about Lilia – I want to know that she and you are one
in deep love and giving.

In Baba's love,

Kaviraj

(George Dowden)

NB: Nobody's buying poetry in England these days.
Except for Blake poetry. I didn't even get rid of
my edition of 125 of the two last books. Have no

distribution in States. Any suggestions??? You coming
to London any time soon? A visit wld. be good.

DETECTIVE CONSTABLE JOHN MARIS ST JOHN CID BY CHRIS COLEMAN (MARKED-UP MANUSCRIPT)

It is the night of the Science Fiction Club at John St John's
friends' across the road. You can see them lit up, through
the window. Willie has a replica blue Spock top on. He is
what is known as a Trekkie. He has set up a small bar in
the corner of the living room and is serving his 'home brew'
from a rustic wooden keg on the counter. Catherine sits with
her legs curled beneath her on the leather couch, her bottle
spectacles, she wears a light blue terry-towelling headband
in her hair, which contrasts nicely, subtly, even, with Willie's
Doctor Spock top. Isobel has a mad perm, she just got her
hair done this afternoon especially. There is an LP on in the
background. Sounds like Roy Harper. There is a younger
girl sat on a high-backed wicker chair. Her name is Madini.
John St John knocks on the door. He has brought some brown
rice cake for the party, sorry, the club meeting. Everyone
hide the drugs! Willie launches into his usual routine. Hi,
John, Catherine says to him. It is so odd to hear him referred
to as John in this story. Or perhaps this is another story,
unfolding.

Tonight's presentation will be on Asimov, Willie reveals,
presented by none other than Asimov-daft Catherine, he
says. Madini sits there looking calm or terrified, it's hard to
tell, but there is something between her and John St John,
in their oddness. Pint of the good stuff? Willie offers John St
John, and this time he doesn't refuse. It is warm and it tastes
of soap and bubble gum.

The presentation has begun. Madini looks like a shrunken woman-child, now that John St John is sat next to her, on a beanbag on the floor. Isaac Asimov was not a good writer, Catherine announces. For instance, his characters are completely flat, and he cannot write women. But I am here to tell you, he was in fact a great writer, even so. Are William Blake's characters rounded? Catherine puts the question to the room. John St John has no idea who this Blake guy is. But Madini nods, which makes him think that William Blake must be the patron saint of freaks. Asimov is a writer of prophetic books, which means books that are *received*, books that are decodings of sensory data into expressive energies, or decodings of expressive energies into sensory data, if you like, because it is a two-way street, bub, Catherine announces, new expressive energies set to decoding possible futures spoken by the *imagination*, which word you could just as well swap for *the voice out of the air*, which words you could just as well swap for *entity*. It was surprising how Catherine talked about Asimov. It was unexpected.

The Mule, Asimov titles one of his characters. The Mule, Catherine continues, is an entity. By The Mule Asimov intends to transmit the idea of evolutionary backroads, however attenuated, and of our ability to travel back there, with what is still present, now, but also it brings to mind the Palaeolithic practice of shamans wearing animal heads – *our* Palaeolithic practice, let us not forget – of wearing animal heads, Catherine underlines, mourning the loss of this prelapsarian state of *knowing* but knowing, too, that the fall into modern mind, from what Asimov terms 'Foundation', to what Asimov terms 'Empire', allows us to travel these same stars, finally, ultimately, these destinations that dreamt of us in the first place, and most of all, to marvel, the gift of marvel is the translation ability of the greatest of sci-fi writers, Catherine concludes, to marvel at all of the new possibilities that will speak to us, just up ahead, on our way back home. *Asimov*, she says, and she repeats his name, by way of finale.

That was it? Apparently, that was it. Wow. John St John is none the wiser. But Madini nods. Curled up like a creepozoid on her high-backed wicker chair. With her odd head like an animal, it is dawning on John St John, now, his own head like an odd animal, too. The roofs of the Palaeolithic caves were our first cosmos, our first point of entry, Madini says. And Willie nods. To the mystery, Willie adds. Then someone brings up the four laws of robotics, and the conversation goes downhill from there.

What's everyone reading? I'm reading *The Fifth Head of Cerberus*, by Gene Wolfe, Madini says. It's just out, she says. I bought it in John Smith's in Glasgow. Do you go into town a lot? John St John asks her; he is attempting small talk, but it is also a reminder of his beat, of how John St John rarely leaves his beat for 'the town'. I am a student at the Royal Scottish Academy of Music and Drama, Madini reveals. You planning on being an actor when you grow up? Willie asks her. Everyone is sat around on the couch and on the chairs, a little bit drunk. Now it's Van Morrison on the stereo. Actually, I already am an actor, Madini says. Oh really, would we know you from anything? Yes, she says. I think you would. Have you ever seen the road safety advertisement featuring the strongman Victor Delgado? Catherine and Willie and Isobel gasp all at the same time. You're the strange kid he uses for bicep curls as he crosses the road! they announce, virtually in unison. God, I used to think that kid was so creepy, Catherine says, I mean, no offence, sorry. No offence taken, Madini shrugs, I'm an actor, she says, I was merely perfecting a role.

What have you been reading, John? Catherine asks him. He's flustered, our boy is clearly flustered, he hasn't the first idea of what to tell them, but then he just comes out with it. I've been reading about spontaneous human combustion, he tells them. SHC, for short, he says. I've seen photos, Willie says. Charred legs in fireplaces. Old women gone up in armchairs, and still in their slippers. Have you ever investigated an SHC? Catherine asks him. I don't know, he says. Maybe. How can you not know? she asks him. I've been to burnings, I've investigated burnings. What was it like? Madini asks him. What were they like, these burnings? The scenes, you mean? he asks Madini, as if it were the backdrop to a play, or a movie. Like ash castles, John St John says, like ash castles on a ghost coast. And now, with its speaking, in this company, it is another story, unfolding.

Afterwards, Catherine is having herbal tea in John St John's kitchen extension. Who is the woman in the photograph, John? Catherine asks him. My angel, my love, he responds. What happened to her? She died. She was never going to live long, John St John says. She had so much spirit, he says. Where does all that energy go? he asks Catherine and no one in particular. That energy is still here, somewhere, he says to Catherine. It has to be. If it were possible to scale the gates of Heaven, he says to her, I would bring her back home to me. John St John is drunk on one beer and speaking like the Bible. Is it possible to scale the gates of Heaven, in your opinion? he asks her. But then, before she can even reply: I'm being blackmailed by her ex-husband, he reveals to her, which is another reason Detective Constable John Maris St John CID is no longer the greatest cop of all time.

PHOTOGRAPH FROM THE WAR WOUND BENEFIT

Fucking hell that looks amazing. Where is that, how can that
be Airdrie, that's Fleur reading in nothing but a one-piece
swimming costume and high heels and a sash that says Miss
Universe on it, she has her hair done up in a crazy beehive,
and it looks like a fucking green luminous UFO is touching
down behind her, this is like the Factory, man, what a scene,
or who is that guy, the hysterical guy, the film-maker, Jack
Smith, *Flaming Creatures*, man, this is as wild a scene as
Flaming Creatures, and someone is leaping from the PA,
there he is, to the sound of poetry, that is the fucking 1960s
right there, an acid prom beauty queen and a weightless
angelic young man taking off into the air to the sound of
poetry, this breaking out of mass grace, it was the decade for
it and goddamn it don't we need another, try coming to these
towns now, set and setting, my friend, I would avoid it, if you
don't want a bad fucking trip, out here it is bad news and
there is no culture and we're imprisoned in our homes in the
grey of these fucking streets and what happened to working-
class avant-garde street culture, where has that impulse been
channelled, the bacchanal of a Saturday-night piss-up and a
kicking on the way home is poor theatre compared to this.

Alongside Alan's dad who was the Zen Buddhist, Fleur
Mayberry's parents were the first true hippies in Airdrie. I
mean, they called their daughter Fleur. And Fleur was the
first true hippy I ever saw. I was waiting at the bus stop at
the top of South Bridge Street when she walked up with bare
fucking feet and just squatted down on the pavement in a
lotus position, waiting for a fucking bus, in Airdrie, we'd seen
nothing like it; it was daring and it was free.

She was a poet and a performance artist. She went to the
RSAMD but dropped out because they were 'crypto-fascists'.

She wrote endless sonnets to her vagina. Everyone was in love with her, she would walk along the high street in Airdrie in a swimming costume and a cape, but she was no one's girl. For a while she had a band with Effie Darrow called Spiderwebs that was like electric folk meets The Velvet Underground but when they heard that Angus MacLise quit the Velvets because he was asked to turn up at a certain time and play for a certain length their mind was so blown by the purity of the gesture that they quit rock music for life.

PACKET OF BIRDSEED

A packet of birdseed. Fuck me, there's a packet of birdseed in here.

BULLET BELT

Bullet belt, from Afghanistan, Alan is on his way into the hills, they have this fucking Jeep Armada and are tearing through the mountains on the way to this compound, this hideout where this cult lives that are probably even now feeding Suzy birdseed in this basement warren, all while they praise some falcon god, and they fuck it, one of the soldiers for hire says to Alan, only they're not even for hire, they're just looking for an excuse, and as they pull up there is this massive security fence which they cut open with wires and they walk in, slowly, pressed against the walls, this is a house built out of the cliff face, a modern villa jutting straight out of the stone, and there is a girl on the phone, a girl has one of those beautiful ornate home phones from the dawn of history, and she is talking on the balcony, with her back to them, the ringleader, Farsi, motions to a garage and they slip inside, one by one, and then into the house by a side door, everyone has their weapons raised, and in the

centre of the living room there is a smoking pyre, there is a
hole, through the rock, up above, and beneath it there are
the smouldering remains of a fire, we may be too late, Farsi
says, as they spread out to search the house, Alan goes to
an upstairs bedroom, cracks the door, there is a man sat on
the bed reading to two young boys from some old parchment,
he puts a gun to the old man's head and makes the sign of
silence, the girl, he says, you took my girl, he's on a massive
amount of this Afghani hash, he's completely dehydrated,
he's mad with rage, where are the falcons, he's saying,
he's asking him where are these falcons that you worship
and fuck to death our girls with, is what he's trying to say,
and the man says, falcons, falcons, the smoke, he says, the
falcons rise up, he says to Alan, and Alan says, my girl,
where is my girl, and the man says, falcons, falcons, gone in
the air, he says, and Alan smashes him in the face with the
butt of his gun, and the kids scream and start crying and
Alan panics, how the fuck did I get here, what the fuck am
I doing here, and there's gunshots down below, Alan runs
out and looks over the balcony, down below there is a full
firefight going on, he kicks open the door of another room,
no one there, and he climbs out through the window, and
down this rock face, all the while this firefight is kicking off
indoors, and it's about a 30-foot drop, but he gets down in
one piece, he has this handgun stuck down his trousers, and
when he gets to the ground he sees a body that has its head
almost blown apart, and he flips completely and just flees the
compound, running out into the hills, like a madman without
a prayer, and he sleeps rough, for the next three nights he
wanders in a daze sleeping rough and drinking from troughs
in these mountain villages that really were single streets
of windowless tombs, and someone said he looked like an
onion, that his beard looked like the roots of an onion, a kid,
passing, said that, and his mother in full burka told him to
be silent, I'm become vegetal, Alan thought, and someone

else said, hey, bro, hey, hardman, nice shoes, because he
was wearing python-skin cowboy boots, and so he avoided
the villages, and headed for the mountains, until he realised
where he had come, somehow, intuitively, or been guided to,
more like, the place of the skull, his own personal Golgotha,
and there he was, this master guru with his dick pointed to
galactic zero, meditating in the eye socket of this stone skull
like the perfect peace he sought inside his own brain, and so
he climbs up this rock face, Alan does, and prostrates himself
at the feet of this guru, and he says to him, Father, and this
guru says, I am not your dad shut up, and Alan says, but I
found you, I found you in all this wilderness, Alan says, and
the guru rolls his blind eyes and says, you found me exactly
where I am, which is no achievement at all, and Alan says,
they kidnapped my girl, they kidnapped and burned my
girl in a ritual, who burned your girl, the guru asks him,
falcons, he says, falcons devoured my girl in smoke, he says,
it's all my fault, he says, she was taken, he says, what am I
even doing here, he says, and he looks around at these arid
mountains with the sun going down, the last of the light,
leaving, the moon, the colour of blood, and the guru lets
him bed down for the night, but in the right eye socket, well
away from himself, and in the morning the guru is in some
kind of state of catatonic possession where he responds to
nothing that Alan asks him, but it doesn't matter, he can
remember the way back to Kandahar, and so Alan sets out
to walk back, and he gets to the apartment and he grabs the
birdcage – why does he do that – he grabs the cage and his
luggage, and he lets the storage facility who were storing
all of the shit they bought know that he would arrange to
have it shipped on, once home, and headed straight for the
airport, where he slept the night on the floor, before jumping
the first flight back to London, and home. Tobias met him at
the airport. The Destroyer and The Disappearer. Reunited.

DETECTIVE CONSTABLE JOHN MARIS ST JOHN CID BY CHRIS COLEMAN (MARKED-UP MANUSCRIPT)

No one has ever been inside a man. There is no space inside a man to be. Or is there. John St John is thinking these confused sleepless thoughts in the night. Every one of us has come from the belly of a woman, he thinks. But what of the insides of a man, he thinks. They are so barren, so inhospitable, incapable of nurturing and of suckling and of growing inside. There is a place inside a man, John St John is telling himself, that is impregnable. Nevertheless, there is a place there, there is a space inside a man, all shut up, and turned in on itself, but there is a space there, nonetheless, and a possibility, therefore, always, John St John is convincing himself. What is a possibility? An empty space inside a man is a possibility. Where are these thoughts coming from? These words, now, on a page? That same empty place inside a man. Possibility. A tomb is inside a man, but not even that. No one is born, or buried there, in the heart of a man. Something lives there, for a time, nonetheless, in man's empty heart where nothing is born and where nothing ever dies; there is life, though no tomb, or cradle, though I long to cradle you, Carol, and make of my heart your sweet tomb, yet you are alive there, neither born nor dying, any more, and but the image is so strong, I can feel you coming through, Carol, your same life force in mine, reflected – tarnished angels, damaged goods, cosmic twins – people would see us in the street and think, what were the chances, how did these two sad cases find each other and fall so much in love – you could see it in the park, in Tollcross, when we went walking – the looks of wonder, and of brief sweet faith that there were more wonderful things in this world yet, and a balm for all the broken-hearted. If you were inside a man, Carol, you would see a distant image of yourself, an image like a cocoon, a fine-spun cocoon all ghostly white, and something of colour, imprisoned there, something of colour, coming through, is this ghostly space in man, this waxing image, of all possibility, is alive in here, Carol.

SECOND PACKET OF UNOPENED OUT-OF-DATE SALT 'N' SHAKE CRISPS

What the actual fuck.

SHEET OF PERSPEX WITH, WHAT, THE ASTROLOGICAL SYMBOL OF AQUARIUS ON IT, OR IS IT

The water-bearer, the cup-carrier.

Industry of Magic & Light resume operations in the spring of 1970. But something has changed with Alan. He's making accusations, wild accusations about people on the scene being on the side of *them*, or listening to stories from *them*, always this *them*, out there, that were trying to get at him, even through his friends, and his inner circle, and of course there's this Suzy-sized gap in the story, this girl who disappeared and never came back, it seems, this girl who was never found, last seen, let's face it, in the company of Alan, whose own mental health was clearly deteriorating, and I don't mean to turn this into a murder mystery but seeing this, something about it, something gets to me about it, a quality of childishness, two squiggles on an overhead projector, the aeon of the child, in all its liberatory patheticness. And how I miss it, all the same.

PHOTOGRAPH OF TOBIAS, THE DESTROYER

This much I know about Tobias. He was expelled from a
local Catholic school for staging an elaborate sonic attack
(involving a recording of the 'sound-poet' Henri Chopin)
on it after he was suspended for being pissed up in charge
of some juniors who he had taken to Benny's chip shop in
Clarkston in order to teach them about 'the poetry of the
streets' and then drove them really fast in a minibus round
the backroads of Plains so that they all leapt into the air and
screamed every time he went over a bump. He was a dealer,
Airdrie's main connection, before he was even expelled. He
tried to survive going door to door selling poetry broadsides,
in Airdrie, in the mid-1960s. He had a long moustache like
fucking Fu Manchu and sideboards like in *Planet of the
Apes*. He said Franz Kafka's journals were his Bible until
he discovered Jim Morrison. He invented a board game
called Cheezers that made him money here and there. He
played fiddle in a ceilidh band called Skedaddle. He lived
in a cottage on North Biggar Road with his gran, who was
blind, thank God. It was rumoured he had contributed
articles to various scientific journals but nobody was ever
clear which ones. He had read every science-fiction novel
ever published. *I have read every science-fiction novel ever
published*, he would announce, *so there is not a single
scenario up ahead that I am not already 'au fait' with*. He
did terrorist activities on behalf of Monklands Dark Skies,
potting windows and panning streetlights. *I would drag
us back to the cave age, motherfucker*, he would say if you
asked him. But then all this technology he was amassing.
At home in this amazing bungalow where him and his gran
would sit in the conservatory, round the back, with tartan
blankets on their knees, and listen to these shortwave radios
that Tobias was restoring, this otherworldly sound, which if
you are blind might as well be the shape of an angel, and he

started collecting synths, stockpiling synths, and one night some people had tried to break in, some boys had heard about his collection and had climbed the fence at the bottom of the garden, but Tobias had spotted their dark silhouettes, and came at them with an axe, and terrified them into submission, and then tied them together and marched them down to the Carlisle Road and tied them face to face to a road sign and went back and told his gran, sure, that's some show on the wireless tonight, and all was well; this guy had a reputation like the Buddha, who, let's face it, was another destroyer.

DETECTIVE CONSTABLE JOHN MARIS ST JOHN CID BY CHRIS COLEMAN (MARKED-UP MANUSCRIPT)

There was a street battle in Shettleston between rival gangs with samurai swords, some guy has been cut up and left on the pavement. John St John walks there from the office; it's only a few streets away. The forensics guy is already at the scene, who we may as well introduce as Joseph, this time, Joseph the forensics guy. Samurai swords, Joseph says, looking up at John St John towering above him in the rain, can you believe this? They've hacked half his neck away, he says, gesturing to a blood-soaked sheet on the wet tarmac. Fancy a peek? he says. Don't mind if I do, John St John says. When he's like this he's inscrutable. He peels back the sheet and immediately a crowd of people are straining their necks over the police tape, trying to get a view of the carnage, eager to see what a savaged dead body in their own street looks like, but John St John tells them to beat it, and some policemen start moving them on. How come he can stand to see it, but somehow we can't, a young wise-ass says, and John St John looks up at him, with his face the way it is, and the young wise-ass is silenced. This is how I can stand to see it, John St John says, to himself as much as to any young wise-ass passer-by. There is a great triangle of flesh missing from the neck. The head is half severed and has collapsed onto one shoulder, the sinews like old burnt rope. A lot of the early samurai were also Zen masters, Joseph the forensics guy – who has a mad Belfast accent, by the way – informs John St John, as he assembles a small white tent around the body, so as not to wash the scene away. These are the scenes, he thinks to himself, only he must have said it out loud as Joseph says to him, what, what did you say about the scene? What a scene, John St John says, I was just marvelling, what a scene, I said. Front-row seats, huh? Joseph says, who is running a little make-up brush along the edge of the pavement while he talks, like a Zen samurai master. What were you saying about Zen masters? John St John asks him. In the tarot deck Swords stand for thought, for cognition, Joseph says. Do you know what tarot cards are? he asks John St John. Are they like ESP cards? John St John asks him. Sort of, yes, they are cards that can be read for divinatory purposes, yes, and they have suits and they have trump cards that are like archetypal powers that every human being encounters in their life. Wow, John St John says, I hadn't heard of that. Well, Swords stand for thought, because they are divisive, they sunder parts of reality from the whole, abrogate it, and then treat it as if it were an independent part, and not a relationship, a doing, a going, which is really what all this reality is. All this reality is a going? John St John asks him. Look, Joseph says, gesturing towards the dead guy on the road, he's wearing sandals, and it's true that the dead guy had bare feet and a pair of brown sandals on. The god that goes, Joseph says, that's where they get the sign of the ankh, the ancient Egyptian sign of the ankh, from the sandal, because we humans, well, we are all process, we are the gods that go. What has that got to do with samurais? John St John asks him. They have perfect

control of the Swords, Joseph says, which means their mind
is like a steel trap. A trap for what? John St John asks him.
For words, Joseph shrugs, as if it were blindingly obvious.
Didn't Zen Buddhists sleep with corpses in order to come to
terms with death? John St John asks him. I wouldn't know
about that, Joseph the forensics man shrugs, that seems a
little outlandish to me, he says, and he goes back to brushing
for some impossibly tiny scrap of evidence that would serve to
explain it all. I need a Coca-Cola, John St John says.
I thought you didn't drink fizzy drinks, Joseph asks him. I
thought you were one of these health nuts. Not any more,
John St John says, and he crosses the road to the Co-op and
comes back with what he calls two 'bottles of pop'. Here, he
says to Joseph the forensics guy, I got you a bottle of pop, and
they both stand there and drink it, in this tent that's being
buffeted by the wind and the rain, with this mutilated body
on the ground, in the early-evening traffic, in the east end of
Glasgow, like it was a cube in space, a white cube in space,
and all around them, intimations of light, and all of the
darkness to see it better.

And now he can't sleep. John St John. He shouldn't have
drunk that bottle of pop. His head is pounding and all over
the place, a spider in a messed-up web. He climbs up into
the loft. He always burns his big head on that bare lightbulb
hanging there, just above the trapdoor. Who doesn't love a
trapdoor? John St John thinks to himself, every time, and we
can imagine him, perhaps for the very first time, as a child
himself, a melancholy, deformed child, exploring the loft with
his father, discovering the magic of a trapdoor, burning his
poor misshapen head on that tender lightbulb, for the first
time, it is like a song has come back to him and he reaches for
the metal rack of 7-inch singles that Carol had left behind,
her collection, she called it, and he pulls out the Dansette, an
old pale turquoise number that is impossibly beautiful and

smells of burnt dust, burnt dust in the air, beneath the eaves, in the loft of his old family home, John St John is spinning 7-inch singles in the night, The Walker Brothers 'Stay With Me Baby' (Philips BF-1548 1967) (G+), Petula Clark 'Just Say Goodbye' EP (Pye NEP-24259 1965) (VG+ but worthless all the same) (track titles: 'Just Say Goodbye', 'The Life and Soul of the Party', 'Hold on to What You've Got', 'We Can Work It Out'), The Honeycombs 'Have I the Right?' (Pye 7N15664 1964) (G), The Beach Boys 'Wouldn't It Be Nice' (Capitol F-5706 1966) (VG), and John St John's heart starts, The Beach Boys, this is surf music, he thinks to himself, this is the music of Jan & Dean, he thinks to himself, Carol would have known what Joseph was talking about when he said The Beach Boys and Jan & Dean, Carol understood surf music, he thought to himself, or did he mutter it under his breath again, and he marvelled, all over again, we can be sure of that, about his Carol, who really was the best, and then he sits down to listen to this surf music, for the first time, and he expected waves, if we're being honest, he expected waves and riptide guitar, even though he has no idea how that might translate into rock 'n' roll sound, but here is a song of children dreaming to grow older, he thinks, wow, it's so gentle, not like a great wave at all, these surfers, playing in the waves, is what it sounds like, didn't Joseph say they never really surfed, surf music is standing in the shallows with your girl and dreaming of the great waves you will surf when you are older, he thinks, and then, what was the goddess in the encyclopaedia that was born from the surf, from the foam, Aphrodite, why, she is the lady of love, he thinks, and he imagines himself, stood knee-deep in the water, embracing the waves and the foam, just like Carol, in her dreams, in her dreams of surf music, he thought, and he felt himself in a triangle then, no longer a white cube in space but a bright triangle, of sound and light and surf, and inside the sleeve there is a note, inside 'Wouldn't

It Be Nice', whose B-side is called 'God Only Knows', there
is a handwritten note, only it seems more like a poem, or
a love letter, truly, what is the difference, and it's hard to
make out, some of it, some of it has become smudged, and
illegible, like tears have fallen on it, and the handwriting is
in purple, who even writes in purple, John St John thinks,
Carol was the very best, he thinks, looking at these violet
teardrops, now, this poem whose only words John St John
can make out are 'shadow' 'moon' 'jackdaw' (?) (is John St
John misreading that?), a French word, *'oui'*, another French
word, *'amour'*, which means love, yes love, it reads, and
there are other words around it that must remain mute and
whose disappearance is relevant to this moment, John St
John thinks, Swords, is what John St John thinks right then,
Swords, and he reconstructs it in his mind, there are black
birds in the shadow of the moon, yes love, there are great
black birds on their way, even now they cast a shadow on the
moon, even now, my Love, they raise the surf, signed Carol
26½ years old, my own true love, yes.

ENAMEL 'UP IN THE SUN' BADGE (RUSTED) (SLIGHT RETURN)

Okay, so what I've found out is there was an inner order.
An initiatory order. Back of Industry and The Old Dragon
Underground, and the initiation was symbolically – or to be
honest, terrifyingly, literally – to be taken up in the sun, into
the light. And then, somehow, 'returned'. Look, everyone is
sworn to secrecy, and almost no one will talk, but then there's
this:

SHEAF OF WRITING PAPER WITH THE HEADING 'ORGANON' ON IT

There was a factory called Organon about a twenty-minute walk from Gethsemane on the other side of the Calder Valley. My grandfather worked there. I've no idea what he did all day but of course my fantasy is that he was part of some kind of project harvesting orgone energy, like Wilhelm Reich at his home, Orgonon, although I think they were into pharmaceuticals, but read it for the poetry, this Organon, across from Gethsemane, sometimes things are attracted to happening just for the play of it, which, truly, was the ethos of the 1960s. And then, written on the paper, beneath the word 'Organon', it reads:

Alan = Osiris
Teddy = Anubis
Tobias = Apophis
Richard = Horus

Behind Industry of Magic & Light there was an Egyptian death cult.

BROKEN MIRROR (AGAIN)

And they built this labyrinth, this intestinal hall of mirrors they would set up in The Abyss, how the fuck did they get all those mirrors, mostly diving for trash, carting about in the van and spotting mirrors, abandoned, mirrors lying by the roadside or piled up with household trash, you probably haven't noticed how many mirrors are abandoned each day in small working-class towns, but when you start noticing, it's weird, mirrors are abandoned as often as single shoes, paint tins and white chests of drawers from MFI in these places, it's statistically unusual, this abandoning of mirrors round here, so they would get high and go on these mirror runs and of course they would be tripping when they would come across these abandoned gateways, these permanent reflections – mirrors never stop, it's intense – which is where the initiation came in with these fucking factory-scale mirror-maze creations – the story is that Alan based it on the labyrinth at the heart of Chartres Cathedral in France – and of course the only way to find your way is to head towards where you are Not, but finding where you are Not in a hall of mirrors is close to impossible, and there were stories about this pop-up mirror factory, where these midnight initiations took place, stories about how some guy had lost his mind in there, after wandering this labyrinth of reflections, this corridor of dreams, on LSD, for the best part of an entire night, and disappeared in there.

PUBIC HAIR

I'm sure that's a pube. I know it when I see it.

The first time I heard about this cult at the heart of Industry of Magic & Light, this inner order of light and dark, was from Cassie, who told me she had been initiated into this mad secret sect but wasn't supposed to tell anyone. We were sat out with the telescope on the deck at Gethsemane, most people had gone to bed, The Butler was crashed out on a hammock across the way. I was on the periphery of the scene, still, but becoming a regular visitor, and they were all cool and welcoming about having me around, except for Teddy Ohm, who early on threatened to 'knock me to the floor and force his dick in my mouth' 'cause I made a joke about R.D. Laing's new book *Knots* being bullshit, and we were lying there, in the night – the night was so quiet, not so long ago, sometimes it's hard to believe now – and Cassie told me, she whispered, Alan has a secret society, she said, do you know, she asked me, and isn't that Venus, I said, high in the sky, that planet there, I said, pointing, because I tried to change the subject.

Cassie told me that when she came to town she wanted to hook up with the art scene, the freak scene, the music scene, the poetry scene, the drug scene, the magick scene and the free love scene, so she had ended up getting initiated, was what she said, in this hall of mirrors, she described it as, and I was too jealous to ask her any more details, not just because they hadn't even bothered to ask me, but also because I was immediately imagining her getting done by Alan and Tobias or, even worse, Teddy Ohm.

But then when I finally gave in and asked her about the effect of these initiations, when I quizzed her afterwards about how it impacted on her real life, she said that it was more like afterwards you see your life as a *perpetual game of dare*. And I imagined so many Cassies in all of her lives, naked, running wild in this endlessly reflecting maze.

SAND

There's sand in here. Was this caravan ever at the seaside? Makes it feel even more like the unearthing of an Egyptian tomb.

A RAINBOW HEADBAND

This is totally Tobias's style.

MISSING POSTER

I brought this along myself, to add to the evidence, to
accumulate it.

> Missing. Alan Cardona. 5ft 8. Dark hair. Medium
> build. Last seen August '75 in the Calderbank area.
> Please call Airdrie 63659 with any information.

Alan disappeared from Gethsemane, which by this point,
in the 1970s, was back to being called straightforward
Calderbank Allotments. He had been living in this caravan,
the last of the hippies, for four years. Vandals had run riot,
crops had been destroyed, tool sheds burnt to the ground.
Working-class villages became vicious places in the 1970s.
Who knows how he survived, entombed, like this, in the past.
There were rumours that he was losing his sight, that he had
begun staring into the sun because he believed there was
some kind of praeterhuman channel that he had an internal
connection with there. He got into this mystic sect from out
of African history called the Sun Watchers, was the story.
To this day, no body has ever been recovered. Taken up? The
Disappearer.

RICHARD BUTLER BUSINESS CARD

This is a real find, with hash burns all over it. Richard
Butler dated my sister, briefly. He was kind of a mod at this
point, although on his card he describes himself as a flaneur,
which is the most mod thing ever. He was so into it he did
home tailoring; the word haberdashery also appears on this
card. He was the sort of guy to bang about with a copy of
Baudelaire in his pocket. And French cigarettes. Sitting in
greasy spoons on South Bridge Street in Airdrie early in the

morning, ostentatiously reading the papers while smoking this French fag and drinking tea probably with a cravat on.

RICHARD BUTLER PHOTOGRAPH

This classic is not a mod. Butler has transitioned, perfectly, from the mid to the late sixties. His mind has been blown. This is taken at Gethsemane, perhaps a little before I first visited there myself, so maybe '68; it's three years on from that business card and here he is wearing dungarees and with bare feet and with his hair all matted like some old mad mystic on the Ganges, his third eye is all squoze out, and he is standing with a bunch of courgettes in his hand – the 1960s was endless fucking courgettes – and he has become The Butler, he has this mad biblical vibe all of a sudden, what's more he has acquired a biblical *gait*.

Did it come from psychedelics, this way he had of walking and of beaming and of looking around himself like it was all so insanely beautiful and completely impossible, which of course, it is? You know that Tim Leary look of pure, joyous realisation? Like finally we are in on this great cosmic joke, this great joy? That was his vibe. But also like this faraway thing in his eyes though, this resolute thing, like there was only one possible way forward, this kind of hardcore acid evangelism. It wasn't *Furthur* it was *Beyond*.

RICHARD BUTLER PHOTOGRAPH

Another classic, just pre-mod; Richard is wearing a suit and holding his electric guitar high alongside three other goobers. This is Butler's first group, influenced by The Shadows and The Tornadoes and The Ventures; Lord and the Butlers. The bassist is Tom Lord, who went on to found Kommandos of

Daath alongside Jesus and Johnny Thompson a mere three years later. Looking at the state of these tuxed-up gimps, it's a real stretch of the imagination. But right here, this is the speed of the 1960s, which, as we have established, is the speed of light.

AIRDRIE & COATBRIDGE ADVERTISER 21/8/1970 (SLIGHT RETURN)

Turns out the boy of seventeen who had taken LSD at an Old Dragon Underground event and leapt from the top of Airdrie Town Hall, like Icarus, was the son of some guy who was high up in the council, and this is when the repression really started to kick in, after the busting of the War Wound, with the shutting-down of events and the denying of permits, and then the death, in custody, of The Butler.

There was a trips festival, in the courts at the back of the Holehills flats, the very same place where Alan's dad had danced a drunken Zen funeral for a dog all those years ago, and the police had broken it up. Only problem was everyone was already tripping. Then there's a food fight. Someone starts a food fight and all of a sudden there are all these courgette dishes flying through the air. There's a skirmish where a couple of police thugs get a hold of Butler's girlfriend, Effie Darrow, and try to drag her off and arrest her, but Tobias and some of his friends beat them back, and Butler and Darrow lock themselves in a flat upstairs. By this time police reinforcements have arrived but Alan manages to talk them down; the situation is out of hand, but there's no need for it get any crazier, he's saying, this is a peaceful party, man, but of course they are looking for drugs, and they're asking why Butler ran, what's Butler and Darrow hiding, nothing, man, but they're up at their door, the police are, and they're taking a ram to it by this point, this is excessive force, and that's when The Butler leaps from the window, he leaps from the window, on LSD, from the second storey of this flat, like he is mirroring the flight of the nameless child (Alex McCubbin), and everyone stops and for a second it is like he is suspended there, like LSD really could alter your relationship to gravity, and then there he was, bearing down on us in this fucking kaftan.

But he survives, somehow, it seems like he survives, he gets up, and the police wrestle him to the ground again, and they have him in the back of a van and off to the station before anyone can do anything about it. Effie goes round and starts taking witness statements and they take photographs of the carnage – all of the pointless carnage – and in the morning The Butler is dead, The Butler is dead, from a neck injury, in a cell, where he had been kept, on his own, coming down on LSD. They said he must have damaged his neck in the fall and that the drugs had somehow kept him going until he died in his cell. LSD has no effect on gravity, but it will extend your life, praeternaturally, even when you are already dead, was the police line. High divers. I think of that phrase a lot, when I think of those times.

WAR ON REALITY STICKER

And then it became more like a terrorist cell, like a permanent war on reality. War on Reality was this campaign they set up, they were trying to inspire a strike against consensus reality, they wanted people to down the tools they customarily used in order to preserve this fucked-up, non-ecstatic consensus of desacralised suffering workaday reality, and they encouraged round-the-clock bacchanal, in the sure knowledge that the sun was both ends burning, even at the darkest hour, and as a blow to old aeon thinking, and to fuck the polis, too. Alan said it was the invocation of a sacred trilogy, the return of the Ur powers, War, On, Reality, which involved renaming the days, somehow, they got this idea from Angus MacLise, the drummer from The Velvet Underground, who was living according to his own calendar that he had created where every day of the year had its own name – 'Day of the Iron Crown', 'Day of the Magic Child', 'Rose Over the Cities', 'The Fire Is a Mirror' – and so they started doing that, too, and it was such a rudimentary act of magic, but so efficacious, so instantly transforming of reality.

This, then, was the second coming of Industry of Magic & Light that culminated in the Battle of Katherine Park and that started with the protests outside police stations, beginning with the station across from Airdrie Library, where hippies were setting up tents and standing around with placards when one of the polis came out and told them that it was just him and Wee Stevie in there and that they would be far better directing their ire at the CID in Shettleston and so everyone decamped over there and for a few weeks there was a protest outside the CID but the locals were just not having it, hippies kept getting a doing, there were random attacks on the protestors, so they went back to street theatre, robes and dosing, the three central tenets of acid fascism, ha ha.

DETECTIVE CONSTABLE JOHN MARIS ST JOHN CID BY CHRIS COLEMAN (MARKED-UP MANUSCRIPT)

The body of a dead hippy is found in a flat facing Tollcross Park; it looks to be an overdose, a heroin overdose – the hippies were bringing this stuff back from Afghanistan – but weirdest of all is she appears to be wearing an Indian headdress. And she is wet. Her body is sopping wet. Can you spontaneously drown, as much as combust, is what John St John is thinking to himself right then.

Around the room there are pictures of American Indians pinned to the walls, this bare room with a single bed and a fireplace and a table, pictures torn from a copy of Dee Brown's *Bury My Heart at Wounded Knee: An Indian History of The American West,* though John St John has no way of knowing this, he has never read a book about cowboys and Indians in his life, but here's Sitting Bull, with his eyes like sad old forgotten lakes in the last of the sunshine, Ten Bears come out of the past like a memory of common origin, Kicking Bird seeming reasonable, a man you could have a rewarding conversation with, Lone Wolf, impossible, and Kicking Bear, wow, what is there to say to a man like Kicking Bear, what a dare, to recognise yourself in him, John St John thinks, as he looks at the corpse that has leaked all over the bed and soaked it. Was it drugs and alcohol that did away with the Indians, John St John wonders, or was it gambling and smallpox, or was it mass murder, mainly, he wonders to himself, until his eye alights on the picture of Big Foot, just above the bed, frozen dead, in the snow, at the battle of Wounded Knee, fixed, now, on a wall in Shettleston.

An arms stash is uncovered in an allotment in Coatbridge after a greenhouse floor is lifted and three boxes of ammunition discovered. A tenement where rubble had been left on the floor by workmen collapses on top of the barber's shop downstairs during opening hours, killing three people. A child is kidnapped by her father outside Garrowhill Primary and they are never seen again. Two dogs are killed using poisoned meat in a residential street in Airdrie. A neighbour describes their incessant all-night howling in the back garden as being like 'dosed goats'. A traffic incident turns into a rolling-on-the-floor fight (at the Baillieston lights) until one guy gets stabbed

with a horse thermometer. An inebriated man challenges
two policemen to a fight in a park in Coatdyke. A boy, barely
eighteen, who had been accused of stalking his ex-girlfriend, is
found dead on waste ground in Barlanark. Detective Constable
John Maris St John CID has been called to a meeting with
his superior. The song on the radio is 'The Long and Winding
Road' by The Beatles. It's Tuesday.

I've always wondered about your name, John St John's
superior, Sergeant Jack Flamingo, says to Detective John
Maris St John, and he pats him on the back as he leads him
into his office by the shoulder, like it is the blind leading the
blind. Maris, he says, as though for a second anyone thought
he was talking about John. I mean, I get John, he says,
self-consciously, as if the book were eavesdropping, John
The Revelator, John St John, he says, but this Maris, what
kind of a name is that from? he asks him. Why has he never
asked him why his second name is Flamingo, is something
that is only just occurring to John St John right at this same
moment, what with all of the sudden focus on names and
their derivations. It means of the sea, John St John says to
him, and instantly, he thinks of The Beach Boys, and surf
music. Surf music is standing with your legs in the sea,
holding onto your girl, while the waves come crashing all
around you, he thinks to himself, though he must have said
it out loud, too, by mistake, because this Sergeant Flamingo
says to him, surf music, you're named after some surf music,
you say, what, like The Fantastic Baggys? he asks him.
What, like The Pyramids? The Pyramids were the baldies
who played surf music, am I right? John St John says. Damn
straight you are right, this Sergeant Flamingo says to him,
damn straight those baldies cut some of the jumpingest surf
sides, he says, 'Penetration', he says, you know that one?
John St John has never heard these legendary baldies in
real life. I have it on the original single, Sergeant Flamingo

says. We should have a record night, he says, spinning
singles, I had no idea you were a surf music man. What
about rockabilly, you into raw rockabilly? Sergeant Flamingo
asks him. John St John looks at him. I came here to be
chastised, he's thinking. Yet now we're going to a rockabilly
party. I like raw rockabilly, John St John says. Like who?
this mad record-collecting sergeant is asking him. Who is
your favourite? he says. And John St John says, Billy. Billy?
Sergeant Flamingo says to him. Yes, John St John says. Billy
is the best, he says. You think Billy is the best? Sergeant
Flamingo says to him. He is clearly impressed. But wait, he
says. Which Billy? Which Billy do you think? John St John
says. Not Billy Fury, I'm thinking, am I right? Sergeant
Flamingo says. You're right, John St John says. Not Billy
Fury, he says. Okay, Sergeant Flamingo says, it's a good call.
It's a good call, he says. Billy Lee Riley, Sergeant Flamingo
says. Am I right? You're right, John St John says. Billy Lee
Riley is, to my ears, the best of all, John St John says. 'Flyin'
Saucers Rock & Roll'? Sergeant Flamingo says. Every time,
John St John says. 'Red Hot'? Every time, John St John says,
and he nods his head, solemnly. Every time. Damn, Sergeant
Flamingo says. Damn, but that's a bold call, he says, and
John St John just sits there looking implacable. You know
I have a fund set up that you can donate to? Sergeant
Flamingo informs him. Kind of a record-collecting pot, if you
know what I mean, he says. John St John nods. I knew you'd
understand, John, Sergeant Flamingo says. It's been good
to get to know each other better, he says, while once more
putting his hand to John St John's shoulder and leading him
the way the blind lead the blind back through the open door.
Call me, he says, my secretary will provide you with all the
necessary details, he says. And before you ask, he says, yes,
I did change my surname because I am such a mad doo-wop
fan. And he closes the door on him, leaving John St John to
contemplate this doo-wop and this rockabilly and this flying

saucers rock 'n' roll that had come into his life and that was Carol's life, really, in the first place.

'THE EXPOSURE OF INNOCENCE IS A LIE' (PATCH)

They wore these patches at the bottom of their denim jackets, and embroidered across the shoulders of their robes, in this gothic font: 'The Exposure of Innocence Is a Lie'. They took it from Crowley's *The Book of the Law*. I've always wondered about that line. The same with this one: 'Deem Not of Change: Ye Shall Be as Ye Are.'

BLACK SABBATH *PARANOID* LP (VERTIGO 6360 011) (POOR)

I can't listen to this album, no way, but especially that damn track 'Planet Caravan', which was the track that Cassie said Alan Cardona had sex with her to, I can't even stand for it to come into my head, she said he just asked her straight out, after her initiation, whether she would like to make love or not, that's what he said, and of course she liked, and she described it to me, he put 'Planet Caravan' on as she unzipped her dress, is what she told me, and what next, I said to her, and she said, well, I sucked his cock, I sucked his cock on my knees looking up at him the whole time with my big eyes (I never asked her what size it was), and then what, well, he raised me up (that's what she said, goddamn it), he raised me up and then he sucked my tits and he got me so wet, oh Jesus, and then what then, well, then, he put his fingers between my legs, and then he devoured me, what, yes, it was crazy, he devoured every inch of me like a hungry man, she said, and then he fucked me from behind, she said, so hot, I was wearing my mother's bra, she said, and afterwards he

told me I was very talented, you're very talented, he said, as I
fell asleep on his chest, oh God.

PAINTING OF EFFIE DARROW BY EFFIE DARROW

There is a painting of Effie Darrow by Effie Darrow in here.
There are about five movements of the brush. The curl of the
hair. The broody smudge of lip. A single pool of blue eyes.
A jawline like a battlement. A long neck. Like a giraffe.
Or an emu.

POSSIBLE TAB OF SHERBET DIP LSD IN A JAR

Okay, this reminds me of the time that I tripped with Fleur
Mayberry and she stuck some LSD up her vagina 'cause she
thought it would make it come on harder, only but she said
it turned her veins into cool electricity, this is at her pad in
the Holehills flats, I'm there with Cassie who is friends with
Effie Darrow by this point, who of course is friends with Fleur
Mayberry, and we're in these flats, who knows if it's night or
day, I'm with these three women, all tripping, flipping singles
– 'Green Fuz' by The Green Fuz, 'Moulty' by The Barbarians,
'That's the Way It's Got to Be' by The Poets – with the first
hippy I ever saw in real life, and Fleur announces the cool
electric fire coursing through her veins, and then she said you
can orgasm in your heart just through using breathing and the
mind, that you could do it without touching, and then she said,
let's have a mass heart orgasm, though I think she may have
used the word heartgasm, and but first she told me to take off
my clothes, he must be divested of his garments, was what she
said, actually, pointing at me, and of course in one sense you
didn't have to ask me twice, but here I was with all of these
goddesses, peaking, these original hippies, coming up really
strong, and as usual with me, my balls had crept halfway
up my nutsack, plus I had an overwhelming urge to take a

shit, but I stripped off and sat down on this beanbag like I
was told, and then the girls all got undressed too, I couldn't
believe it, without a word, or a sign, like the moment was now
magic – all three took off their clothes – their long dresses and
kimonos in pools on the floor, my eyes are at the exact level of
their thighs, and what is the word for that, that crease at the
top of a woman's thigh, that place of desire, so beautiful, that
virgin crescent is forever, I thought to myself, tripping right
there on LSD, and now they are sat around me in a triangle,
Fleur in front of me, Cassie to my left, Effie to my right – with
her pale Pre-Raphaelite looks, and red hair, her dark brown
nipples – there's incense burning, and they all three of them
close their eyes but I can't bring myself to do it, I'm doing it for
the sake of eyeballs everywhere, what a sight, these goddesses,
vibrating now, together, and it's true, I'm getting this feeling
in my heart, rising, through breathing and concentration,
through this triangle of hippy goddess, and Fleur is wearing
a black turban, I forgot to say so, she has a black turban on
with a coiled snake brooch on the front, and the breathing
is so soft now, and so sensual, you can feel it on the hairs of
your arms, I see their eyelashes flutter, their curled eyelashes
flutter, butterfly kisses, is what you call it, and I feel it too, I
feel the centre of my consciousness drop, and the heart is alive,
and is speaking, with such joy, it is like I am filled with light,
and then Cassie and Effie start this chant, it just happened,
Cassie said yes, out loud, at one point, and Effie said forever,
in response, just beneath her breath, and then we were caught
in the rhythm, all of us, systole and diastole, the first lovers,
it felt like, the twins, yes, forever, yes, forever, and who
couldn't climax with that rhythm, I felt it travel up my spine,
this rhythm from the beginning of time, this atom of pulse
that speaks yes forever, everything they say in the Indian
guidebooks is true, the garden of the heart, and right then I
understood, perfectly, the difference between Golgotha and
Gethsemane, and how you could be crucified between them,

the organs know, they know more, these three goddesses, and I have just been initiated into the secret of ecstasy, and now I'm here, in this temporary shrine – ecstasy, caravan, language – for everything we do with no hands.

LETTERS TO A YOUNG POET BY RAINER MARIA RILKE (PENGUIN 1968) (GOOD)

I remember seeing this exact copy of Rilke's *Letters* in Alan's hut, in Gethsemane. It was so small – a hermit hut, really – he was living close to destitution, in a way, but somehow it still seemed beautiful, and free, and adventurous. He had this hut with a deck on one side where he would sit out in a dashiki, this dark blue dashiki with gold, and with a pair of sandals on, and this huge gone-to-seed beard at this point, like passed-out-in-a-bath-period Jim Morrison, and inside his hut was about maybe four metres by two and he had like an old chest with his duvet and sleeping bag stored in it that passed for a table, and there were two wooden chairs, and a triangular cupboard in the corner with a Ganesh on top and a psychedelic eye painted on it, and along the floor on one side there was this old Afghan carpet, folded two or three times, and that's where he slept, he just lay on this carpet that by day was covered with cushions and that passed for a couch and there was a massive old rusty stove that you couldn't believe still worked and then a table, a table that served as a place to write and work and prepare food and then he had added a greenhouse extension so that it ran on about another three metres and in there he had lots of little wooden tables and wooden ladders and everywhere you looked he was growing plants, there was a bed of wild flowers along the window, and on the table that was just a trunk, really, just a basket with a lid on, there was this copy of Rilke's *Letters*, along with a poetry collection by D.H. Lawrence, *Birds, Beasts and Flowers*, and a book called *The Tower of Alchemy*, is how

I remember it. I was eating everything up, back then. I was so hungry for all of it.

That night we sat out on his deck, I was with Cassie, and Effie, who was still heartbroken over the death of The Butler, it was April and Venus was beautiful in the evening sky, the days of Venus, we passed around a bottle of wine with the firepit blazing, that divine smell, of fire and of women's hair, looking up at the new night sky, like the first humans on Earth with eyes to see it, and afterwards Alan got really drunk and incoherent and said he was going to head off and screw this wee Polish number that had moved into a hut just along the path, and so the three of us slept on the Afghan rug that night, in Alan's hut, on the floor, together, with the windows open and the owls hooting, these two beautiful women curled up by my side, and in the morning we skinny-dipped in the Calder, as if every spontaneous pleasure was free, and come true. That was the story of the 1960s, brother. Bummer if you missed it.

UP IN THE SUN #1

They only went and printed their own fucking newspaper and sold it on the streets.

WHERE IS LIGHT COMING FROM IN MAGIC AND SILENCE?
BY THE BUTLER

There are realms, out there, beyond the barriers of time and space, that are unimaginable to us mere beings now. Yet even today, the veils are parting, the mistress is inviting deeper knowledge, further seeking, and we have come to learn of presences in our galaxy that have the autonomy of gods. We name these quasars, black holes, photons. We name them: light.

There are multiple suns, is the truth. Our world as heliocentric presents a first revolution. Then: galaxies. These galaxies are infinite. Galaxies within galaxies. The furthest smudge is a further galaxy. Light is the only way to measure its depths. Galaxies are expanding, but where are they expanding to? Stars are speaking. The light from stars is information-rich, is autobiographical, is like the first novel, forever. We learn so much about a star in how it shines, how it transmits, how it speaks to us in light. How warm are you, baby? Do you need something? What are you lacking, honey? Where are you going? Light is tender in how it talks, too, and sweet.

Early man gave personality to the heavens. In that they were scientists. Crystals were the first to talk to certain radiances of light. They interpreted light in a way that eyes on their own could not. Then, as when a thing happens, other entities were attracted to this particular sphere of activity, and soon light was speaking through a multitude of new medias.

Mediumship, as any scientist will tell you, is the first boat launched in any attempt at contact. For instance, quasars are impossible to approach outside of metaphors, outside of the comparison of ourselves to ourselves, yet they obey rules unimaginable to ourselves. They insist on being seen, yet their energy is out of all explanation without approaching the question of the Nightside, which is Not.

Now we are witness to the collapse of stars, what then. The death throes of stars throw out so much stardust that is the birthplace of stars. And these atoms are inherited and live forever; we are all made of star stuff. The sun is always the sun, until it explodes, and becomes a white dwarf, and then a neutron star, which takes us back to pulsars, neutron stars and black holes, so dense no light can escape, but they are not holes, the terminology is all wrong, rather they are hyperdense, which again brings us to this Nightside, again, black holes as the seal on Daath – Knowledge – the secret sephiroth. Whose formula is Silence + Magic = Light.

Recognise yourself yet?

DETECTIVE CONSTABLE JOHN MARIS ST JOHN CID BY CHRIS COLEMAN (MARKED-UP MANUSCRIPT)

John St John has removed a tile from the ceiling of his kitchen extension and is up there in the ceiling with a ladder. His head has disappeared into the space above so that only his body is visible. It looks like he is wearing the whole room for a head. He is wearing slippers that look like smart Italian loafers. Otherwise, he is dressed unremarkably. In a dressing gown. In a red-wine-coloured dressing gown. If that is unremarkable to you. It is to me, but that is only because I have seen him in this dressing gown most evenings. Though I failed to point it out. Previously. I believe I am fatigued with its sight. Now he brings down a Spar shopping bag stuffed with money. Now he's counting it out on the table by the light of a small lamp. It looks creepy, out behind him, in the garden. Occasionally he sniffs some of the notes. Perhaps these are the notes Carol hid down her nylons. He separates the notes into two equal piles, and he puts one of the piles back in the bag and hides it, once again, in the ceiling of the kitchen. The belt of his dressing gown has come undone and for a second there I thought he would trip and split his head on the linoleum, but no. He turns on the radio. The fate of the unnamed opponent of Maurice Yushenko has been forgotten in the silence of his coma. Instead there is static, the sound of between stations, and shortwave wow and flutter. Surf music.

The next day John St John deposits half of the money in an account whose details he was given by Sergeant Flamingo's secretary. But first he goes to the library, at lunchtime, to read a book he has ordered on tarot. He is sat among the large-print science-fiction volumes towards the back of Tollcross Library; whether his positioning is deliberate, or not, is hard to read. He finds out there are four elements behind the tarot's ordering of the world, Wands (Fire), Cups (Water), Swords (Air) and Disks (Earth), all of which, themselves, are passing through cycles of one to ten. There's a whispered voice in his ear, his ear that looks like it has been used as a chew-toy by an awful dog, let's be honest, and it's Catherine, of course, in the large-print science-fiction department of Tollcross Library. Your fate is sealed, she whispers, and she makes John St John start, for a second; he's getting jumpy, this one, what on earth has become of that old cop calm, but then Catherine says, only kidding, it's not, and he notices the large-print sci-fi book in her hand, *The Time Machine*, it is called, and he says to her, what's that about, and she laughs and rolls her eyes and she says, oh my God, man oh man, you are too much, she says, it's about a machine that travels in time, she says, it's right there in the title, and John St John asks her whether she believes in time travel, only what he actually asks her is whether she believes in the *possibility* of time travel, and she says, no, she doesn't, time travel doesn't exist, Catherine says, and she looks cute in her glasses, it has to be said, and that one little tooth, that slightly protrudes, beneath her lip, that's cute too, now that you notice it, and she says, you see, I don't believe in evil, she says, and I think the only evil I can imagine is time travel, but seeing as it doesn't exist that means that evil doesn't exist either, because if time travel existed the world would have been wiped out long ago, because you can bet the first thing people will try to do with time travel is to go back and right historical wrongs, and to take vengeance, and to wreak justice, and that would be the end of everything, all of this delicate mess, she says, and John St John looks at her for a little bit, in silence, it is like he is resigned to something, to some course of action, despite himself, and then he says to her, you like to read books about evil, and she cracks up laughing and has to admit that, yes, it is true, she gets a thrill reading about the *possibility* of evil, is what she actually says, and John St John thinks to himself, I will bring down all of these Swords and Cups and Magic Wandacles to bring her back to me, is what he is thinking, right then, time travel and evil, or not.

MISSING POSTER

Another Missing poster, this time for Jamie Witherspoon, last seen 15/3/70. I added this one, too. If this were a crime scene it would be totally corrupt. But there's a connection. When Jamie Witherspoon disappeared a letter had been found, a letter inviting him to an 'initiation', an 'initiation' that he never showed up for, supposedly, according to interviews the police made, yet they were expecting him, in this factory of mirrors, because the maze had been completely set up, and weirdly it had been left set up – the lights still flashing on and off in who knows what occult rhythms, the insane body-vibrating drone still playing, the infernal loops still spinning, the mirrors, still alive in there – because when the police looked into it they turned up and they found this fucking mirrored maze all set up and who knew what to think, what the fuck are they doing with this improvised labyrinth of reflections, this corridor of dreams, in a backstreet in Airdrie? And they looked into it more and they thought, wait, the reason they hadn't shut it down, the reason they had to flee, was that something went terribly wrong that night. This is pure Gnosticism, I said to myself, when I saw them in the streets with their black robes and their weird insignia, a war on reality that was taking place in Airdrie, right now.

PHOTOGRAPH OF A WEIRD OCCULT PARADE, 1971

This is when The Old Dragon Underground commandeered a bunch of floats and just stood on them motionless on the backs of trucks in full black-robe regalia as they drove through the streets of Gartness and over to Chapelhall and up through Calderbank, who could ever forget that.

ON HAVING NO HEAD: ZEN AND THE REDISCOVERY OF THE OBVIOUS BY D.E. HARDING (THE BUDDHIST PRESS 1961) (VG)

This was a massive book for so many of us back then. It was the first book I ever came across to openly trade in spiritual ideas as if they were available right now without any sense of having to earn them or study them or otherwise 'qualify' for them. Harding's practice is to come to see that you literally have no head, and no two eyes, neither, and that there is no observer, that all the time we are living conceptually, and not experientially. And that everything comes out of, and back into, the void; every thought, feeling, love, doubt, came from nothing, and went straight back there. Just for the hell of it. And that you are not contained, rather the Eiffel Tower and the Taj Mahal, the Bosporus, and the mermaids and angels that swim in it, the very planets themselves, and further out, quasar, star, are the very blood and corpuscles of the mind: image. Hippolytus, in *Refutation of All Heresies*, writes, 'For already have I become a boy and a girl and a bush and a bird and a silent fish in the sea.'

DETECTIVE CONSTABLE JOHN MARIS ST JOHN CID BY CHRIS COLEMAN (MARKED-UP MANUSCRIPT)

Gladioli. Gladioli take their name from *gladius*, because they resemble Swords. John St John knows this because John St John is a keen gardener. He is working in his greenhouse today, though really, his father's greenhouse, because it is the weekend and he always takes the weekend off, unless someone dies, which is almost every weekend at this point. But it appears no one's life has been taken with any degree of suspicion this particular weekend, and so John St John is free to tend his plants. That's when he realises gladioli are Swords. Correspondences, are what these are known as, the reduction of all experience to its elemental components, of which there are four. Wasn't God's name spoken by four letters in the Bible? Next to John St John's garden there is an electricity sub-station that generates an unearthly hum at unexpected and ungodly hours. Right now, it is humming. It is humming in a high frequency. Which is why John St John has the radio on in his father's greenhouse, in order to blot out the noise with a semblance of peace. And how he hears that the unnamed opponent of Maurice Yushenko has woken from a coma but cannot talk or otherwise communicate other than stare in abject paralysed terror from this coffin, this awful cocoon he is buried in. And for some reason he thinks of his father right then, of his father's passion for roses, and he thinks of Swords then, too, and this furious sound is rising, in the background, as Maurice Yushenko's unnamed opponent is given a name for the first time, spoken, on the radio: Adam.

IMPOSSIBLY TINY CLOTH BACKPACK

They came up with this idea. Pigeon delivery of drugs in the Monklands area. The doos were big in Airdrie, in Coatbridge, all along the Calder and the old canal. Butler came from a

birding family and they were dyeing these pigeons all sorts
of crazy colours like it was Jimi Hendrix let loose, which
was how they got lifted, obviously, in the end, because
they couldn't send out just like a normal fucking pigeon in
disguise, they had to send these homing pigeons through
the skies, with these same miniature backpacks on, only
with like purple wings with lightning-white streaks and of
course glimpsed from the street, in real life – up there! –
these pigeons looked amazing, but it became like that old
urban myth about how when someone has hung a pair of
gutties on a telephone wire it means there is a dealer in
that street, well, every time you saw a psychedelic pigeon
it was a batch of LSD or homegrown grass on the way to a
distributor, so that psychedelic pigeons, everyone will tell
you about the psychedelic pigeons, if they grew up in Airdrie
and Coatbridge in the sixties, and the 1970s, nobody will ever
forget it.

PHOTOGRAPH OF AN ORGY SCENE

I was never into orgies. I don't know why, too controlling,
maybe, too challenged, perhaps, lack of confidence, maybe,
absolute disinterest in naked men with cocks, certainly, but
Cassie was. Yes, she is in this picture, spearing me through
the heart, while getting speared, in return. Her feet in the
air. This boldness, which absolutely appals me when I see
this, this licence, this same licence that drove me wild, that
drives me wild, this is Cassie, this was Cassie, I remember
her explaining how she couldn't understand how anyone
who truly loved someone wouldn't be happy that their lover
was never denied any possible experience, any indulgence of
sensuality, any beautiful one-night stand. We want the best
for each other, right? she would say. We want for each other
all that the world can experience, right? Free love. And she
would call herself the Astonished Woman, named after some

book by a madman. What about the Astonished Woman? she would ask me when I got mad. And of course, as she says all these things, I only want her more, I only want to hold on harder, the more she is able to let go. And still I'm holding on, with this caravan, this temporary shelter, still holding on. The Astonished Man. Carve that on my gravestone, as my true name, when I'm gone. Until then. What.

THE ASTONISHED MAN BY BLAISE CENDRARS (PETER OWEN 1970), NO DUST JACKET (VG)

Here it is. I just read it. Okay. Okay, so this guy Blaise Cendrars says he realised himself as the Astonished Man when he was fighting in the First World War (a war where he lost his arm), when a member of his troop was exploded in a bomb, and he had literally disappeared before his eyes, blasted into the void, taken up, into the sun. That was the moment when Cendrars realised himself as the Astonished Man. Astonishment is holy ecstasy and awe. And quaking and terror, too.

I lost my job. I lost my job because I was dropping out, and becoming unconventional, and unreliable, too. They were probably right to let me go. I became a full-time bum and I moved into a hut in Gethsemane on a section that was known as the 'Green Mile', more for the amount of marijuana grown there than for the length of the path, and I had nothing but a mattress up on pallets and some blankets, and some books, it was the summer, and so I dragged the mattress out onto the deck, and slept out in the open air for the first time since I was a kid, and I woke up feeling dewy, and born again.

ANOTHER SUMMER BY CHRIS COLEMAN (DARKSIDE BOOKS 1971) (VG)

That's me, that's my book. My first novel. My debut. Set
on an island. A poet in love. Across a single summer. I am
always going back to a single summer. The summer of 1970.
Okay, so I put this book here myself so I could talk about it.
I wrote it in the hut. In Gethsemane. On a typewriter. I was
bereft when I wrote it. Cassie had gone back to West Virginia
to look after her mother who was dying of cancer and who
would write her the most heartbreaking letters. I have lost
weight, and I feel so sad, she would write to Cassie. And so
she headed off, to nurse her into death, to minister to the
dying, while I sat out on the deck in the evening when the
clouds were peach and black and I wrote this book, imagining
it was possible to lay hold of anything, to preserve a perfect
summer forever, and I didn't think about writing anything
else, till years later, till now, in this caravan, where all
these words lie, because after a few letters exchanged things
petered out, until finally she never wrote back, my Cassie,
and though I wrote her several letters, several heartbroken
pleas, I never heard from my Cassie again.

DETECTIVE CONSTABLE JOHN MARIS ST JOHN CID BY CHRIS COLEMAN (MARKED-UP MANUSCRIPT)

Yes, perhaps. Perhaps it will be possible, Alan Cardona
tells John St John. Alan is meeting with him in his kitchen
extension to discuss necromancy. There is a long history of
necromantic workings, Alan tells him, it is the first magick,
the one most dreamt of, and there are many books and
instructions available. It often involves the desecration of a
grave, Alan has to admit. But John St John is nonplussed, how
else would she rise? And Alan says, that's a good point, I never

thought of it like that, that's a good point, he says. Then John St John changes the subject. Your friend, he says, referring to Carol's ex-husband, your friend is becoming a pest, he says. He's costing me a lot of money, he says. There's nothing I can do, Alan shrugs. That's between you and him. Then John St John changes the subject once again. Do they come back different, do you think? Are they changed, the risen dead? he asks Alan. In my experience, Alan says, I would have to say, yes, they aren't quite the same. You've had success? John St John quizzes him. You've risen the dead? I had someone come back, once, Alan admits, though I'm not sure I would call it a success. Why? John St John quizzes him. They came back changed. By death? John St John quizzes him. The dead have experiences? I no longer call them the dead, because they can come back, Alan tells him. I call them the taken. And the returned. She may find me changed just as well, John St John says. Perhaps it is the dead that never change, and us, instead, who are unrecognisable in them, Alan says. Because they have been made perfect, and we would have them debase themselves, all over again. But Carol returned as perfect is all that John St John can hear.

'AIRDRIE UNDER PSYCHIC ASSAULT?' HEADLINE FROM *APACHE* NEWSPAPER (COPIES AVAILABLE FREE FROM THE WAR WOUND)

The streets of Airdrie, its monuments and architecture, its parks and catacombs, its flats and council houses, its car parks and estates, its glens and quarries, its observatories and old people's homes, its ice-cream shops and bakers, its deserted garage forecourts and gone-to-seed hotels, its grim old flats and hidden-away mansions, seem to be some kind of omphalos for the ingression of a fleet of angels.

CHERRY BLOSSOM

I am lying with Cassie in the grass beneath a pink blossom
tree when I see an angel in its branches. It is hanging upside
down from its toe like an acrobat on a trapeze. We had been
up all night tripping and had fallen asleep in the grass and
on waking I was greeted by this show-off upside-down angel
who reminded me of the time that I had been sick, as a boy, I
had been poorly, and this angel said to me, with a voice like
a lone birdcall at the very end of the world – a chirrup – that
this was in fact the very same angel who had come to me as
a little boy, this very same angel had held hands with me
in early moments of fright, for I am a ministering angel, it
announced to me, and what is your ministry, I thought in
return, and it said, amour, ministry of amour, it said, and
I said, can I ask you something, and it said not now, and it
disappeared, because Cassie was starting to stir, and she
said, were you talking to someone, and I said, was I talking, I
thought I was just thinking, but it was out loud, Cassie said,
I heard a voice out loud like a bird, she said, and I said, who
speaks like birds, and she said, angels.

ANGEL PAINTING BY CASSIE

Angel painting signed Cassie.

USA/JAPAN JOURNAL 1966 BY TEDDY OHM (SELF-PUBLISHED) (VG)

This is a true rarity – a self-published facsimile of the journal
that Teddy Ohm kept on his legendary trip to New York and
Tokyo in 1966 to visit his first two gurus, the artist, musician
and filmmaker Tony Conrad, and the author, actor and poet
Yukio Mishima. How he got in touch with either of them,

indeed, how he even funded the trip, remains a complete and total mystery. But he saw The Velvet Underground play the Balloon Farm, which must have been a major influence on The Old Dragon Underground, and of course he hung with Tony Conrad, visited the Ludlow Street flat, was completely dismissive of Lou Reed, loved Moe, said Conrad was a genius, MacLise too, Lionel Ziprin is in here as well as Ira Cohen, plus Harry Smith (the first time he ever did peyote with Smith, Teddy said, he realised he had a 'Native American soul' that meant he could 'see for miles'), oh, and Nico too (no spoilers!) and then he went to Tokyo to study Noh theatre with Mishima and you can see him in the background in the film *Patriotism or the Rite of Love and Death* where, it is true, he looks uncannily like Cher playing an American Indian. It makes me think of Teddy's other guru, and of hubris, and of fatal flaws. (SERIOUS OFFERS ONLY)

FOLDER OF COLOUR PHOTOGRAPHS

— *We are at a crash pad in Coatdyke. I am sitting in the sun, on the balcony, smoking a blunt. There is music in the background. Someone has put a record on. Soft Machine. It is an album by Soft Machine.*

— *A day out, on bicycles, to Plains. We sit in the soft sunshine and drink mushroom tea. We cycle to Caldercruix in the sweet sunshine.*

— *Now a group of us are fishing at the reservoir on a glorious summer's day.*

— *Now we are pictured naked on the shore after leaping into the cold water. Fleur's make-up is run like Julie Driscoll, her cheap panties are forever.*

— *I am reading a book about Egypt, lying on a beanbag in the afternoon, the light is come through the coloured glass like in a humble church, a single log on the smouldering fire.*

— We are swimming in the Calder, it is the perfect day. It is
     so warm, we all get up in the morning, the rest of the crew
     arrive, and we run down to the river, in our underwear
     and our swimming costumes, discarding our clothes as
     we go, and we dive in, we all dive in, only it's shallow
     there, and Tobias cuts his shin on the rocks on the bottom,
     and there is a streak of blood in the water, a beautiful
     streak of blood flowing downstream, and Effie climbs up
     on the bridge and strips off and balances precariously on
     the bridge, she is performing some poetry while marching
     back and forth, naked, and then she leaps from the bridge
     and throws herself in, and afterwards we are all sat up
     on the grass, lying back on towels, reading, smoking –
     someone gets a bonfire going – and we grill vegetables,
     someone is reading Kafka and says, what a belly laugh,
     The Trial is such a belly laugh, don't you get it, it's Fleur,
     and now she is playing chess with Teddy Ohm, who when
     he is wet looks like an ancient American Indian, and now
     Teddy has taken Fleur off to teach her how to shoot water
     rats with an air rifle.
— Carol drops off the children. She can't conceal
     her disgust. After she's gone, John and Avril pick
     strawberries beneath the green nettings.
— It's feast night, and Alan has set up his old military
     yurt with a dining table and chairs and everyone
     helps out with the cooking. We roast a leg of lamb with
     rosemary from the garden and new potatoes. A fresh
     mint sauce – wild mint is growing out of control all
     around the allotment – and those smells take me back
     there immediately. I see Alan slide his hand onto Cassie's
     thigh and she doesn't make any attempt to push it away.
— We are watching Super 8 footage of Gethsemane filmed
     by Teddy Ohm, at Christmas, in the snow. The camera
     zooms in on a chimney with the smoke slowly rising
     and spreading out, above the snow-covered roofs, above

the huddled handmade homes. Everyone is silent and reverent of this sweet smoke, rising up there, in the past.

— I walk Cassie to her car and take a shot of her leaning against it in a dark blue dress and a neckerchief. She is holding onto her hat in the wind.

— A party with the pantheon of Egypt rendered in papier-mâché heads. The women are topless around the bonfire.

— Someone has made a threat, an anonymous note, about the toplessness, the headlessness, the licentiousness, and Alan has acquired a shotgun from a taxi driver he knows, he tells me, by way of explanation, as if all taxi drivers have weapons concealed, and a couple more air rifles, too, he adds.

— The police arrive at Gethsemane. Carol reported us after Avril asked her what 'the occult' meant. She told the police that I was exposing her children to a black magic cult. They said they wanted to come in and have a look around, that no one should actually be living here, but seeing as it's a private allotment, and not one owned by the council, they couldn't enter, and they left after a brief conversation.

— My wife sits on the steps of our first house with our first baby in her arms. The past seems so fantastic.

— Now she is come through the door and is kissing me on the cheek. Her unbuttoned shirt, a little glimpse of her bra, drinking wine on the couch and watching TV and falling asleep in each other's arms. And sometimes she would go to bed and leave me on the couch asleep and I would wake in the night and not know where I was and it would take me a while to realise I was still at home and not in some unimaginable adventure of my dreams. But then I would slide into bed, and feel the sweet warmth of her body, the warm silk of her nightdress. Dreams exist to exhaust this life, I would tell myself. And besides, what else is there to do?

DEFLATED WATERBED (WITH THE LOGO 'HANNA' ON IT)

Waterbeds, everyone was crazy for waterbeds in the 1960s and no one was crazier than Rab Hanna, better known as Sinew Singer, the pop star, though really the true rock 'n' roll star, of Airdrie in the 1950s and early 1960s. Teddy Ohm turned us all on to him, he had all his singles, – 'Tracing Paper Moon', 'I'm Affected', 'I Made a Promise to Rock You' – he said he was a psychedelic avatar, like Eddie Cochran, and of course Sinew had got his name from the time he had been looking in a friend's scrapbook and they had cut out a picture of Elvis and Rab had asked them, what's that guy's name, and this friend said, it's the new singer, only Rab heard it as it's Sinew Singer and his mind was completely blown, this guy whose every sinew was exploding in song, wow, I'll have a bit of that, he thought, when he found out he had just misheard it and that really the dude's name was Elvis fucking Presley, and he committed himself right there to being a rock god for life, he took on the name, though more properly, the mantle, of Sinew Singer, and now Teddy had this whole scheme, he wanted to relaunch his career, this guy is the father of all of us, he would say, which was almost literally true if you counted the number of illegitimate kids in Airdrie that claimed parentage from him, only Sinew wasn't keen on coming back, I'm staying true, he said, I'm staying real, buddy, he said to Teddy Ohm, and got right in his face, no one ever spoke to Teddy like that, I was amazed, only Sinew Singer could get away with this, I thought to myself, and he said, I play the raw shit, sunshine, he said, this ain't no Billy Fury bullshit, he warned him, no Marty Wilde joke, my friend, this goes straight to the source, Sinew said, and he grabbed his balls and thumped himself in the heart with his fist at the same time. And I don't need the

money, man, I'm not in it for the filth, my friend, he said. I'm
stacking dough with this waterbed business, he said, believe
me, I don't need no package tour. This is no cabaret shit we're
planning, believe me, groover, Teddy reassured him. I'm
thinking you headline the Katherine Park protest gig and
we get Kommandos of Daath to be your backing band. These
guys are hip, Teddy said, this is the real underground shit, he
said, no compromise, he said. Can these faggots play electric
blues? Sinew asked him. This is beyond electric blues, groover,
Teddy said. And with that, the deal was done. But not before
he sold Teddy a circular waterbed that Teddy used to sleep on
in this mad underground bomb shelter that he bought off the
government where he was storing a second copy of every record
he bought just in case he had to go to ground 'cause of the
apocalypse and that he had paid for by running a drug cartel
with the Two Daves. These hippies were nothing but fucking
brilliant businessmen.

Alan and Rab – sorry – Alan and *Sinew* had a special
relationship. Sinew would turn up at the huts, he loved to
be around the hippy girls, and Alan would get him a bottle
of rum and some Coca-Cola and we'd all sit around on the
deck, me and Teddy and Tobias, and Jesus, and Tony and
Johnny Thompson, and Fleur, and Effie – Cassie was gone
by then, Richard dead – and just listen to his mad tales, like
how he turned up at Prestwick Airport in 1960 with an air
rifle intending to shoot Elvis in the ass 'just to scare him, you
understand', how he had to 'carry Dolly Parton around an
airfield on my shoulders once' – a feat he refused to elaborate
on – how he had received a secret charter from the Oakland
branch of the Black Panthers because the B-side of his 1957
single, 'Tracing Paper Moon', 'Dark Side/Black Rhythm',
was a kind of underground anthem there. I could officially
set up a Panthers cell in Airdrie, Sinew boasted, if I took
the notion, he shrugged. And Alan was keen; fucking Black

Panthers in Airdrie, man, total solidarity with our brothers, he said, even though we don't really have any brothers right now, in Airdrie, he admitted, or any who need a black radical paramilitary organisation to stand up for them, quite yet. What about that groover that teaches at Airdrie Academy, what's his name, Forrest? Teddy Ohm said. He seems to be doing fine though, Alan admitted, I don't think he has any real need of guerrilla justice right now. Keep me posted, Sinew shrugged. I can activate the charter whenever.

WEDDING PHOTOGRAPH OF CHRIS COLEMAN AND HIS LATE WIFE CAROL

I keep this in my wallet, I don't know why. My wife Carol died at the age of 32 from complications arising from an underlying condition. My mother took on guardianship of our children. I never attended the funeral.

DETECTIVE CONSTABLE JOHN MARIS ST JOHN CID BY CHRIS COLEMAN (MARKED-UP MANUSCRIPT)

It is the last night of the Science Fiction Club, or our last visit, more properly. Of course, only you and I and John Maris St John know this, that he will never again return, that things will never be the same. Quick, hide the bong! Willie jokes, as usual, when John St John makes his entrance. Hi, John! Catherine says (and yes, it still feels weird when she does that). Isobel brings him his customary sticks of celery with their ghastly dip that he never dares touch. Madini is propped up in a corner like a dead child on a throne. I see your house is on the market, John, Isobel says to him. No! Catherine says, she is wearing her cute oversized milk-bottle specs, you're not leaving us, John, are you? John St John perches awkwardly

on the beanbag. I have to move on, he says. I have lived in
that house all my life, he says. The route I walk to work, he
says, is the same route I walked to school. John St John is
in a strange, confessional mood. He speaks like these are his
last words on record. What book are we reading from tonight?
he asks the assembled friends, breaking the still spell of his
confession, his confession that he has taken the same route
through life, every day, and then we remember the time he
walked back home barefoot, on that same route, and suddenly
there is more longing in John St John's actions than we have
been able to notice ourselves, we who bang on about attention,
and Catherine says, we are reading from *Dune*, by Frank
Herbert, she says, and he asks her, what is that, what is
Dune, and she says *Dune* is a planet made of sand, an endless
desert, and John St John imagines walking barefoot in the
sand, once more, of stepping into the waves, once more, hand
in hand with the woman whose love he loved, of being taken
up, in the surf, and the light, into the sun, once more, and he
says to the room, a planet made of sand, an endless desert, is a
nightmare to me, for my middle name is Maris, which means
I am *of the sea*. It is as if he is singing his story to them. How
many more begin-agains are we allotted in this life? he asks
the room, and everyone is silenced. There will come a day
when we can no longer begin again. Not today, he said, and
he shook his head, not today, however. I have chosen to begin
again, he said, and with that he bit into a big stick of celery
with a sound that didn't seem quite so smug this time round, a
sound that was more of a calm resoluteness, perhaps, though
that could just be the circumstances talking, but then again,
however to silence them, and everyone took turns reading from
Dune and when John Maris St John read from the 'Songs of
Muad'Dib' by the Princess Irulan, the part about the fallen
seas, when he sang it, there, so softly, it's fair to say that
everyone was in tears.

GRATEFUL DEAD 'BORN CROSS-EYED'/ 'DARK STAR' 7-INCH (WARNER BROTHERS 7186-WB) (VG-)

The studio recording of 'Dark Star' by the Grateful Dead, released as a 7-inch single in 1968, condenses the entire arc of the psychedelic moment into two minutes and fifty seconds.

EYEWITNESS ACCOUNT OF THE BATTLE OF KATHERINE PARK

Katherine Park was kind of an early hippy hangout where you went to make the scene. Most people weren't really into boozing, psychedelics cured a lot of us of that, plus we saw where it got our parents, and so hanging out in the park in the daytime and getting high was a big deal. And Katherine Park was always kind of empty, except for the inevitable alcoholics who lurked around the gates drinking like they had no council house to go to, so you didn't really tend to get harassed, especially when it became associated with heads, because you would see cute young kids turning up and, like, wearing shades and strumming atonal acoustic guitars in the grass, looking to be inducted into the future. But then there was this move by the council to sell it to some property developer. And of course we were in the middle of this war on reality and of course we were paranoid, and high, and it seemed to us, whether correct or not, we will never know, that the council were selling it precisely because it had become this liberatory space. There was always this feeling like The Man was out to clamp down on fun at all costs and in dour fucking Church-of-Scotland Scotland it's well fucking founded.

So there was an ongoing occupation. Semi-occupation. More presence, really. We had this slogan, Save People's Park, though when we said people, we meant hippies, because most of the people who lived in the nearby courts kept out of the park, precisely because of hippies, and of course there was the further problem of the Two Daves taking over a garage down there and manufacturing LSD. The Old Dragon Underground would stage Happenings in the park, there was always music, someone busking, a people's corner, where you could get up and rant about whatever you wanted, providing it was pro-hippy, naturally, and this is when you're beginning to see the same old orthodoxies of any 'belief' or 'movement' solidifying. The Battle of Katherine Park, for me, was the defining moment, when the revolutionary period of hippiedom was over, the moment when nobody knew what it was, or who they were supposed to be, or what could possibly happen next, was over, and suddenly it was being performed, it had become an orthodoxy, new rules, but rules all the same, and Katherine Park, at the time of the occupation, was the first time I saw people dressing up as hippies, because it was the thing to do, and of course you can say to me, well, weren't you the same square that had to dress up like a fucking hippy in order to escape your suburban marriage, and I hear you, did I really want to escape it, did I do the right thing, did I throw away something beautiful, is there peace in the suburbs, is there happiness there? Yes, I guess, for those that can find it, and maybe I, too, found it, by wearing a mask at first; what is that tarot card (The (Lovely) Star) where the woman is wearing a mask of stars that she clearly cannot see out of, as she follows her own particular star, and although she has broken her chains, she still wears bracelets around her ankles? She is not entirely free, but she would be, as she dips a single toe into this great waterway that would take her out from the fixed, from the patterned, from the determined, out into the wild of the world; this star is me, too, even though in my cynicism I couldn't recognise this same star in others.

We hired a bunch of generators from this place in Coatbridge and the day before, which was a Friday, this blazingly hot

Friday, we got a crew together to build the stage. The idea was that Industry of Magic & Light would perform onstage, with the bands, so we lined the back and sides and the roof of the stage with mirrors.

Now, let me just underline, this was a totally legal and above-board festival we were holding – for a change, ha ha ha. The council had caved and allowed us to have this mad event because they were getting worried about the protests, and back then no one knew what the fuck the kids might do next, so let them have it, was the attitude, all the way to the major labels, if you think about it, the culture was transforming at such speed that you were forced to just roll with it, or at least make it up as you went along, because back then no one could guess the shape of the future. Except for us, maybe, ha ha ha.

With the passing of The Butler, Tobias had taken Effie under his wing, she was his old lady now and they were cute on the day, he was wearing this mad woollen poncho and she had these mad dungarees on, it was one of the highlights and the best memories, those two. Effie and Fleur both read on the afternoon poetry stage, and there must have been a hundred people by that point, for poetry, why should that be so unbelievable now, a hundred people all sprawled across the football pitch at the far end of Katherine Park listening to Fleur's now officially banned poem 'My Menses', I think your man AB was dead by then, but Ian Cunningham read that afternoon – whatever happened to that guy, specs and a duffle coat – and of course Effie read her amazing *Welcome Death Cycle* of poems and the War Wound had a stall selling books, and there were stalls with pipes and bongs and Da Capo Records had a stall – sorry, two separate stalls – and of course Sinew had insisted that he be given a free stall to punt his waterbeds, which were flying out the door, it has to be said, and then when the evening drew in the atmosphere totally changed.

It was our own fault, perhaps, we were pushing too hard, we were all totally out there, we were starting to believe our own myth. So everyone who is working for The Old Dragon Underground is given these black robes that Teddy Ohm had apparently made himself, apparently he had The Butler's old sewing machine in that fucking nuclear basement of his what next, and the robes had hoods and sewn onto the shoulders in ornate red thread were the words 'The Exposure of Innocence Is a Lie'. Then some kid got burned because there was a procession of these hooded figures across the park, right through the centre of the crowd, just before the music started, and it was startling and it was dramatic but it was ridiculous too, because they had made these fucking torches by just wrapping some bin bags around some fucking wooden sticks and of course as they made their way across the park the fucking plastic was melting and dripping everywhere and some kid got some on his leg and started screaming, and someone else got it on their robe and it melted right through and clung to his flesh and he was rolling on the floor and trying to stub himself out, and of course it's early evening by this point, people are starting to come up, and of course the Two Daves have made this 'tribute' LSD, especially for The Old Dragon Underground, the legendary Vocokesh tabs, and of course it looks like these fucking headless warrior monks are setting themselves on fire, are immolating themselves, right in front of this whole field that is basically tripping as one, this combination of mad occult theatre and complete and utter stupidity, and of course I'm doing it, I'm walking along with this fucking torch sputtering everywhere, and but then the music starts and it's a fucking relief, it's fucking Gryphon, back, again, fucking Gryphon, what is this shit, I honestly can't remember a thing about them, were they like

Traffic maybe? Did they come from Coatbridge, Bargeddie, somewhere like that? By this point there's honestly about 400 people, it's getting out of hand, no one expected this many, and there's just a weird vibe, a weird vibe, I dunno, Alan is a little shaken, this could very easily get out of hand, he's saying, they can do anything, he keeps saying, they could be anywhere, he says, always this fucking indeterminate they behind the scenes, pulling strings and setting shit up, but Teddy loves it, this is high magick, groover, he says to him, this is the game we came to play, he says, and he reassures a visibly shaken Alan who is already on too many drugs, while Tobias, well, Tobias is love-struck, he's out of the game, he's not picking up on any vibes outside of Effie and him rolling in the grass like kids backstage, and then Sinew arrives, Alan and I arranged to meet him at the Two Daves' garage across from the courts and I'm not kidding, he looked like a cross between Link Wray, an Apache Indian street killer and Elvis '68. Black leather boots, black leather jacket, black leather trousers with black wraparound shades and a necklace of brightly coloured feathers. Fuck me, Alan whispered when we saw him up ahead, but I am tripping balls right now. Sinew was there with his wife, Kathy Cowgirl, and his little girl, Mary, who was dressed like an Indian squaw with a feather in her hair. Sinew was sweating it; he was not happy. Where's the transport in and out? he asked us. What are you talking about, man? Alan said to him, it's just at the end of the street, what did you expect, a fucking helicopter? Listen, sunshine, Sinew said to him, I'm a fucking underground legend here, I don't just walk through the fans like a fucking . . . serf. What an insult, he said, and he spat. This is fucked, he said, and he spat again. I need to touch down on that stage like a fucking close encounter; do you know what I'm saying, I need to shop up like a sudden alien, he said – I always remember those phrases, *a fucking serf, a sudden alien* – look, Alan said, there is no clear way through, I can have our troops (he called them troops, I remember that) clear a passage, and we can get you through that way. But I can't be seen, Sinew insisted, I can't be seen. Okay, the best we can do is a bedsheet, in that case, Alan said, and I totally thought it was going to be the final straw right then, but Sinew just said, cool, we'll do the bedsheet, it's kind of a classic, he admitted, and Alan laughed and said, ha ha, normally more for fugitives from the law, or from the press, or for mental cases out on remand, he said, and Sinew just looked at him and said, what exactly the fuck do you think I am, and Alan was silenced and he got the Two Daves' driver, Wee Tips, to nip across to his mum's house in the courts and get a fucking duvet sheet and they started walking Sinew up the street, towards the park, covered in this big fucking duvet, and of course he can't see a fucking thing, and he's stumbling this way and that and then the fucking rumours start, well, the fucking rumours had already started, Teddy had been putting out the rumour that Dylan was gonna break his self-imposed silence with a secret gig for The Old Dragon Underground, a local warm-up show, in Airdrie, and when everyone sees this guy wrapped in a duvet they all start shouting, Bobby, fucking Bobby, Bobby D, and kids start running towards us and we're trying to guide him and protect him at the same time, and he stumbles and falls, and the girls are all over him, but he holds onto the duvet, his wife and his daughter are just looking on in amazement, he won't let them get the duvet off, and eventually some of our troops come running down and create a little space, a little corridor, but everyone is still screaming about Dylan, it's Dylan, Dylan's here, and we get backstage, Alan has had a caravan towed to the park to serve as a backstage area, and everyone is told to get out and make room for the Singer, and Sinew takes his duvet off and we're all getting ready for him to just kick off about the chaos and all he says is, well, first he shakes his head as if waking from a dream, and then all he says is, when they find out it's me, all hell's gonna break loose. And so it did.

There are people with banners with paintings of The Butler on them and banners protesting deaths in custody, banners proclaiming Katherine Park a 'Free State', banners that just say Fuck the Polis, banners that say Save People's Park!, banners for legalising marijuana, banners for flowers, and love, and freedom, banners for Kommandos of Daath, banners demanding Fuckface The Eagle: Pay Us What You Owe Us, banners for the War on Reality, somewhere on the fringes a brave family have a banner demanding Justice for Jamie. The Zodiac Killers take to the stage. Tobias and Alan start in on the visuals.

The Old Dragon Underground are distributing tabs of Vocokesh throughout the crowd, they're stage-managing some kind of Happening, they're looking to force its hand.

The Zodiac Killers have driven from West Kilbride in an ice-cream van. Kind of a rural CSNY vibe with a lead guitarist called Tonto. As it gets darker the mirrors come into their own. At points it is like staring into the sun. Then The Monarchs of the Night Time, Airdrie's greatest garage rock band, take the stage. Locals were starting to turn up, attracted by this incredible show of light, you could see it in the skies over Airdrie from miles off, reportedly, from Coatbridge and from Holytown, this light of industry, somehow returned, and mirrored, oddly, and The Monarchs are playing this supremely snotty, power-crying loser garage, like the early Stones only but with more fuzz and more lovelorn minor-key testimonials, songs about bad girls, and chicks being unkind, as well as a massively sneery version of '(I'm Not Your) Steppin' Stone', there was a dark, droning, repetitive soul-music thing they had, too, and it's true that their manager Fuckface The Eagle, this madman from Yorkshire, ran dubious accounts and was a dangerous hardman, modelled after Grossmann, to the point that he insisted on eating the same cheese as him, which he had imported, specially, this mad expensive cheese they all got

into in Woodstock, plus he was into holding concert promoters
by their two legs out of tower-block windows, but after The
Zodiac Killers' endless strung-out jams they really got the
crowd pumping only but then the police show up, the police
show up and some of them are on horseback, a lot of them are
on horseback, actually, Wee Nimmo Adams breaks the news
backstage, it's the equestrian division, Wee Nimmo announces
– he was a smart wee bastard, even though everyone used
to sing this mad song about how they're stinky and they're
smelly, they can't afford a telly, their mother's name is Nellie,
the Adams Family – it looks like they are trying to surround
the park, he says. Me and Teddy and Wee Nimmo grabbed us
some flaming torches and crept round the back of the park and
it was true, there were lines of polis on horseback silhouetted
against the horizon like Revelation. Holy fuck, Teddy said,
they'd really do this to us, he said, they'd stomp all over us,
he said. The fucking pigs. I was starting to get the fear, the
Vocokesh was coming on. I was starting to get streamers,
things were wobbling, and who knows what happened to time
because right then it was time for the headline act.

Kommandos of Daath took to the stage first, on their own,
and started up this extended jam, this extended fucked-up
jam that was in waltz-time, for fuck's sake, and it's trippy
as hell, and Jesus starts to rip into this solo and Industry of
Magic & Light drop to this pure white light, this white light
domain, is how I can only describe it, this *white light domain*
that is strobing through all of these mirrors like it might just
fucking be about to give birth, and then fucking Sinew Singer
steps through the mirror and onto the stage and it is as if he
is born from pure white light and instantly you realise what
they are playing, what they are jamming, what they have
been jamming all along, it's 'Morning Dew' by Bonnie Dobson,
the folk song, they have been jamming this epic version of
this post-apocalyptic anthem right from the start, and at that

moment it all clicks, as Sinew unravels the mic from the stand and starts to sing the lyrics about walking out on the new first morning and about the simultaneous impossibility of ever beginning again, but yet the necessity, of lighting out, into the soft morning dew, and the place explodes, my honey, of course it does, the place just explodes, my love, and at one point Jesus takes a second solo and Sinew leaps off the stage and runs, like a fugitive – we thought he was off, but no – only to embrace his wife in the audience, his darling wife Kathy Cowgirl – who knows what was going on at home – and they dance, then, together, he embraces her and they hold each other close, to this music about walking away into new mornings, they waltz to this wall of wailing acid guitar, they hold each other so close, in this new light, it is mind-blowing, and then he kisses her hand and he climbs back up and goes into another verse about tears and crying and choosing not to listen and the crowd are freaking out, you can feel the presence of the horses, the silent horses in the distance, snorting, ranged around the perimeter of the park like a terrible reckoning, and right then Alan and Tobias turn the lights on the audience themselves – the oils are like hieroglyphics, the white light and the mirrors, blinding – and right there, is the true beginning, and end, of the 1960s, right there, the exact moment Sinew sang about never seeing anyone ever again, all of us, every one of us, disappeared – for a split second, a split second that is impossible to substantiate, now, a split second that is inexplicably lost, but a split second that happened, once – and we entered the mirror, together, and everything fell silent, and the field was empty, and in its disappearance the 1960s will live forever, in the silence of Katherine Park, in its complete abandonment.

They say it was the lights that caused it, that they were spooked. Because it was then that the horses charged.

DETECTIVE CONSTABLE JOHN MARIS ST JOHN CID BY CHRIS COLEMAN (MARKED-UP MANUSCRIPT)

FIRST DAY OF QUEST

John St John is at his last day of work looking at the corpse of a horse that has had its stomach torn open. A horse whose stomach was torn apart by an unknown assailant during the Battle of Katherine Park. A poor suffering animal that is now dead. What did they say about the soil from a grave and an immolation and a sacrifice? Joseph the forensics guy is marvelling at the wound. It has been completely disembowelled, he marvels. Wow, he says, the stomach is completely torn open, he says, and he shakes his head in amazement, someone must have used a huge, serrated blade. Or a sword? John St John asks him. Sure, Joseph says, swords could inflict this kind of damage, without a doubt. John St John moves his hand towards the wound and gestures. Do you mind? he asks Joseph. Be my guest, Joseph says, and John St John inserts his arm into the gaping wound up to his elbow. Wow, he says. Wow. Light spooked the horses, and they stampeded into the crowd, John St John said. It's a miracle no one else died. John St John slides his hand out of the wound and into his suit pocket and he fiddles around in there. He has a mound of soil, or is it ashes, in his pocket. I'm taking some time off, he tells Joseph the forensics guy, this poor horse has completely done it for me, he admits. By the way, he tells Joseph, I heard your Beach Boys. Surf music, huh, well, how do you like it? Joseph asks him. 'The Warmth of the Sun', John St John says, do you know that one? I don't know that one, actually, Joseph the forensics guy admits, was that one of their hits? It's an early one, John St John admits, you probably wouldn't have heard of it.

Back in the office, Liz asks him if he is looking forward to his break. Yes, he admits, I really am, John Maris St John admits, I could do with something a little bit different, he says. Thank you for all your kindness to me, John St John says to Liz, and especially for the cassette you gave me. It has been a great solace to me, he says. They stand there, awkwardly, but they were never going to embrace. Then John St John packs the contents of his desk into his brown briefcase and bids her farewell, farewell for now, he says, to dear Liz. On his way out he calls in to see Sgt Jack Flamingo. Hi, Jack, he says. Hi, John, he says. We're all set, John, Jack says. The bulldozers are going in tomorrow morning. The owners want it flattened. There will be an end to this, he assures John St John. Don't worry. Or a new beginning, John St John says. Then he says, I heard the pyramids, and it isn't immediately clear whether he means the baldy surf-rock group whose big hit was 'Penetration' or whether he heard the actual Egyptian pyramids, the tombs of the great pharaohs themselves, speaking. Either way Sgt Jack Flamingo made no attempt to clarify and simply asked him what he thought of them and John St John just nods and says, good.

He leaves the CID on the Shettleston Road and walks back home along the same route he has walked all his life, only for the last time, this time, which makes it feel like the first time ever, that same desolate graveyard, those same stinking pubs, that same grim primary school, that same strange modernist church, those same haunted bungalows, this same desolation, those same tenements, in the early-evening light, aren't they beautiful, this same garage with its field of flowers where he first picked flowers for his mother, and for his darling Carol, and then home to his mum and dad's house, for the last time, which is the first time ever, now, what a thrill, where he removes the rest of the money from the kitchen ceiling and adds it to the contents of his briefcase, and you're left to wonder if he really had heard the pyramids of Egypt speaking and that he believes, like the pharaohs of old, that he will require money and goods on the other side.

He takes a bus to Airdrie, the last bus to Airdrie – suddenly it is important – and makes his way to an address, an obscure industrial building in the backstreets off Forrest Street with a single letter above the door: A. On entering The Abyss he is greeted by four figures in black hooded robes with the words 'The Exposure of Innocence Is a Lie' on their shoulders: Isis, Anubis, Ra, Horus. He is given something to drink – some kind of psychedelic concoction – and is led through the curtain to the room of mirrors, where he is left alone – though more truly he is *abandoned* – with his endless selves. At first the mirrors are silent. But then there is a rending sound, a tearing sound, the sound of something travelling at impossible speed in order to arrive here. Do angels tear the hymen of the light? And now it is impossibly loud, like white noise, like the sea, like the sound of your own blood, in your ears – surf music, John Maris St John thinks to himself, in a final thought – and there is a sound like mirrors smashing, like mirrors cracking and collapsing, like great speeding birds crashing through mirrors, and he steps forward, he looms, John Maris St John does, like the greatest cop ever, he steps forward again, and again, he looms, with great daring, his hands are balled up like fists in his pocket, and again, he steps forward, through the noise and the light, and again, with great daring, until he takes that final step, up, and into it, until it yields; unearthly city:

Afterwards, there is no one there. John St John has perfectly, disappeared.

PART TWO: MAGIC

0. THE FOOL

ADAM

I went to Prague, this was the time of the Iron Curtain, I was
travelling from East Berlin, and I turned up at the central
square in the city, a square whose name I can't remember
now, and asked for a man called Coy who was one of the big
men there who could help me out with a job. Only when I met
him for an interview I had taken too much speed and all I
could say to any of his questions was yes, yes! Even when he
asked me my name, I replied like this, yes, yes! He obviously
thought I was an imbecile and so after he said to me, hold
on here, let me think about this for a minute, he offered me
a job selling sunglasses to tourists out of a suitcase in this
same main square that escapes my mind. Only the thing
was that I was colour-blind. And I was supposed to display
the sunglasses according to their colour. And of course I
kept getting it wrong, and I got so worked up that I said
to this big man Coy that I was colour-blind, that was why
I was messing up, and he said to me, okay, let me think
again, he said, and then when he came back he said, okay,
I want you to sell these things that had like the texture of a
nut, like a shell, and inside them were these carved wooden
beetles with wooden legs that wobbled when they moved –
there were no imports from China back then – and he said
to me, you can sell these on the square, only you must tell
people you are a Czechoslovakian artisan craftsman who has
made them himself. Only but I couldn't speak Czech, so Coy
came up with the idea that I was a mute Czechoslovakian
craftsman and had another Czech guy speak on my behalf
while I gestured with my hands and made weird semi-
audible voices like a man who couldn't speak talking. At the
end of the week Coy asked me how my takings were, and he
looked at the tally and he said, this is not good, this is really

not good, and I exploded, finally, and I said to him, what more can I possibly do, I am already impersonating a mute Czechoslovakian craftsman, for God's sake, and he said, okay, let me think, wait a minute, and when he came back he had a sheet of green cloth, which he draped over the table and placed all of the wooden beetles on, and then he said, beetles, in the grass. After that my takings went through the roof.

SUZY

On 22 February 1967, you go to see the Jimi Hendrix Experience, Soft Machine, The Flies and Sandy & Hilary at the Roundhouse. The new rock music is a revelation. Afterwards, the guitar tech for The Flies spots you in the audience, this tough, handsome hippy with a sexy boil on his cheek, this denim-clad hippy who intimidates your boring boyfriend, Dave, whose passive manner you read so much into, but at least he got you guest passes, so thanks, Dave, but bye now, and he leans over to you, this biker-hippy-roadie type who smells of aftershave and gasoline – his breath is honking, honestly – and he whispers something in your ear, something that we may never know, something commonplace, probably, but stated boldly, and with conviction, and you are so smitten, right then, he is so forward, this rocker, that right then big dull Dave is history.

And then your father dies, and then your mother, shortly after. Your father who promised you all of your childhood that for your eighteenth birthday he would get you a nose job or a car, and who of course never got you either. Still, you inherit a substantial amount of money. You buy a flat off Portobello Road where you get involved in primal scream therapy with a rogue practitioner who is later arrested for sexual irregularities. The handsome roadie goes off to tour America with The Who and is never heard from again, except for when he dies falling from a lighting rig during an Alice Cooper gig.

On 30 May 1969, you attend the Harvest Records showcase at the Roundhouse featuring Third Ear Band, Michael Chapman and the Edgar Broughton Band. You meet Alan Cardona there, who at this point still looks like Chris Hillman from The Byrds (he's that handsome) and who is living in a VW bus down a cobbled lane in Hackney. He's on his way to Afghanistan, he says, he is doing the hippy trail, he says, he's going to bring back rugs and cushions and robes and coats to sell at a head shop in Scotland, he says, and you feel the call to adventure, and you say that you will go with him, this Alan, that you will throw your lot in with him and go see the world, and yes, maybe find yourself, out there, too, while you're at it, yes.

THE · MAGICIAN

I. THE MAGICIAN

ADAM

Coy found me an apartment. Sharing with three Germans
and an Ethiopian. It was in the attic of an old apartment
block. One night we discovered a boarded-up door that
opened onto all of the attics in the block, and we dropped
down into someone else's room, stole a portable TV and set it
up in the kitchen with five chairs round it. As the Ethiopian
watched TV, he would roll cigarette papers into balls and flick
them with his finger into the bin until one of the Germans
threatened to cut his finger off. One night we watched a
documentary about ancient Greeks in Delphi where they
used the word omphalos, which means navel of the world.
But the youngest German said it was bullshit. Everybody
knows Prague is the belly button of the world, he said. And
I said, well, what was it once connected to, in that case. And
he said to me, what in hell are you talking about, this young
German with shoulder-length blond hair and a moustache.
And he said, the navel is where you are born from, and I said,
no, the navel is the connection to where you were born from.
And then he told me to fuck off. You fuck off, I told him, you
ignorant Kraut spiv, I called him. I don't know why I called
him a spiv, except that maybe he wouldn't understand it and
think it was even worse than it is. But he knew his English
fine. A fucking spiv, is it? he said to me, and he pushed his
chair back as if in a challenge. But right then Coy arrived,
and he said, wait a minute here, what is going on here, he
said, and we said we were arguing about belly buttons, and
whether Prague was one, and whether you were born from
one, or not. And he said, man is born from a pussy. Woman
too, he added. Not this shit about belly buttons, he said. And
inevitably everything calmed down.

I just remembered to tell you that the beetles were bought as
a job lot because most of them were damaged. At night while
we watched this stolen TV I would sit at the kitchen table
and fix their legs, and glue them back on, and sometimes
the Germans would say, hey, give me a sniff of that glue,
faggot, and then they would laugh, as if they were just being
friendly, although really, they meant it. And the Germans
would sniff glue, two of them, that is, while the young one
with the long blond hair drank tall glasses of Pilsner and the
Ethiopian picked at his bare feet in sandals and flicked the
hard skin into the bin all over again until one of the Germans
threatened to cut his toe off.

Then one night there was this mad banging and cursing
against the secret attic door and we knew that someone had
got wind of us making away with their telly. The Ethiopian
split the scene. The Germans, two of them, were on glue.
The other one was drunk. I had swallowed a wrap of speed.
Without thinking or even taking stock of the situation, I
opened the secret attic door and just punched this guy in the
face as hard as I could and he went flying backwards and I
honestly thought he might even have gone through the ceiling
with the force of it, and before he could come around I got the
two Germans who were on glue to help me carry him over to
the hatch above his room and drop him back down there. For
all we knew he might be dead but the Germans were in awe
of my punch, and they kept replaying it and miming it and
exaggerating its speed and the precise angle of its 'upward
thrust', was what they called it, and comparing me to boxers,
to Mexican boxers, mostly, because of my size and my stature,
they said, I didn't know anything about Mexican boxing then,
but they said, yes, Rafael Herrera, who was on a roll this
year, they said, Chucho Castillo, they said, and they made up
names for me, The Clawhammer, on account of my surname,
and The Nine Pound Hammer, or just The Hammer, and they

called through the Ethiopian and told him he had missed out
on some real action, and the young German with the long
blond hair said that he was sorry he had told me to fuck off,
and that he had no quarrel with The Hammer. Then when
Coy turned up to collect the rent the Germans insisted that
I replay the whole thing for him and Coy was impressed and
said I had a right like a cobra. Then he said, wait a minute,
let me think about this, he said, and then he said, yes, wait,
I've got an idea, and that was the last time I ever pretended
to be a mute Czechoslovakian artisan selling beetles in that
main square that escapes my mind.

SUZY

You are asleep in the back of the van, in a bed built up
against the ceiling, beneath a sheepskin throw, you are
asleep in your lover's arms, it is the autumn of 1969 and you
are somewhere in Austria, high above a train track, next to
a tall forest with great gloomy cliffs, the fog has hidden the
mountaintops, and you are asleep in your lover's arms, the
stove, blazing, in the early-morning chill, the distant sound
of the night trains, down below, it is a delight to be out here,
you two, making love in the back of the van, it is all decked
out with rugs and throws and with candles, you are the only
light in sight, out here, where are you, somewhere in the east,
you were recommended this place by a guy wearing a beret
sat with a pet alpaca on the steps of a cathedral in a town a
hundred miles back who reminded you that it doesn't get any
better than this. Since then, you have forded three rivers,
travelled through storms and sunshine, and seen packs of
wild dogs, roaming free. When you make love with Alan you
say his name, you repeat his name to him, again and again.
You say, Alan, oh Alan. Or sometimes you say, yes, forever,
yes, forever.

THE·HIGH·PRIESTESS

2. THE HIGH PRIESTESS

ADAM

My new job was to be Coy's minder, which at first
meant just as much pretending as when I was a mute
Czechoslovakian artisan selling dancing beetles out of
wooden nuts in the square. I never thought of myself as
a tough guy. But slowly I gained confidence. I started
training. My posture improved. I shaved my head. I got
a tattoo that said 'Wrecking Ball' from a guy down a lane
in the old alchemist quarter, I don't know why I did that,
later I got it covered up with a picture of a dragon. I started
hanging round in parks doing sit-ups on climbing frames. In
the summer I walked around with no top on and my T-shirt
trailing from the back pocket of my shorts, plus I never wore
socks. One time I took a crowbar to the Vespa of the head
of a rival team that was trying to muscle in on Coy's part of
the square. Mostly I just stood around, trying to look hard.
You looked hard back then, Coy would congratulate me,
very good. Then I burst a guy's head open over unpaid debts
and I got a real taste for it. I started going to fight nights
that the local gym would put on at a sports centre on the
outskirts of Prague in an area of abandoned warehouses;
it felt covert and bloodthirsty. I started boxing myself,
and I won my first three amateur fights, one on points and
two by TKO. When I finally knocked someone out, in my
fourth fight, the Germans were at the front, screaming for
me, as was the Ethiopian, who was with a blonde woman
with a tattoo of Marilyn Monroe on her bare back, as was
Coy, who all the way through shouted, yes, murder him,
yes, and of course what I didn't tell anyone was that I was
on amphetamines and could have killed a horse had it
stumbled, all confused, into the boxing ring, but the thrill of
taking another man's consciousness and subduing it, briefly,

even permanently damaging it, in the name of sport, on drugs or not, was like a spiritual revelation.

We ended up going back to someone's apartment where they had a pole from a strip club in the living room and I think I had sex with the Ethiopian's girlfriend, which is why I know she has a tattoo of Marilyn Monroe on her bare back, although what I don't know is if the Ethiopian knows I slept with her because I was too drunk to remember whether the Ethiopian had even come back to the party at all, and of course the Germans couldn't remember if they were even there themselves because two of them were glued out of their heads while the other was ill with the beer.

SUZY

By a wild mountain lake, so turbulent and pale, Alan is urinating into the waves. He is silhouetted there, wearing a floor-length army coat, his hair caught in the wind, as it begins to snow. In the morning you are snowed in, the van is going nowhere, and so you sit it out. Alan cuts sodden firewood in the snow with a scarf tied round his face and you combine it with the last of the dry wood you have; it turns the glass on the stove green, but still it feels heavenly, sunk in all this snow, in this terrific sticky heat. Alan is writing in his journal and you are sketching him, writing in his journal, by candlelight, miles from anyone else, how could they find us, and in the background the snowy trail, and the forest, and the turbulent lake.

THE·EMPRESS

3. THE EMPRESS

ADAM

When I was your age I could have jumped over that fucking
house, Coy said to me the next day, pointing to a wonky
three-storey apartment like they have in Prague and
haranguing me, even though I had a hangover. You have
the whole world out in front of you, he said to me, you can
do anything, he said. I want to puke up, I said. I wish I was
your age, he said, I would take over the world, he said. He
was becoming my mentor. What do you intend to do with it,
he said, and he gestured all around him like he was Atlas
himself hoisting the entire world onto his shoulders, and I
said to him, I intend to be the best fighter ever, even as I
could feel my dad right that second looking over my shoulder
and saying something mocking about how God's plans will
see about that, or something just as mean about the vanity
of all earthly ambition. Then he gave me a copy of an album,
Freak Out! by The Mothers of Invention, as a present for my
win, and that was the next thing to blow my mind because
'Trouble Every Day' became my theme song.

We went to an underground concert, my first concert ever,
me, the Germans, the Ethiopian and Coy, and we all did LSD.
These guys are our very own Frank Zappa, Coy insisted,
plus there's a psychedelic light show as well. At the time I
didn't know what a psychedelic light show meant. The music
was discordant and didn't change much. But the girls were
beautiful. They wore long, flowing dresses and thick eyeliner
and danced on the spot like witches. I got talking to a girl at
the bar but when she asked me what I did I told her I was
a boxer, which wasn't even strictly true, I was more like a
bodyguard or a bouncer, and she said to me, bummer, man,
'cause I'm, like, a pacifist. And I said to her, all women are

pacifists, it's not as if they have to go to war or start fighting criminals in the street, and she said I was a male chauvinist pig to boot and walked off. Then the main band came on. I thought they had been on already. And maybe it was the LSD. But I started to get it. I mean, I grew up listening to Elvis, of course, and Little Richard, and best of all Eddie Cochran, and this music was like a split second of that music only extended forever, like a magnification of that music, I thought to myself, like an atomic vision of that music, and I thought of atoms, and of splitting the atom, and of how that was how it all had come about in the first place; and that's when the devil appeared to me.

Only it felt like someone had dropped a bottle on the floor and it had smashed. Only this is in my brain. And the next thing I remember is this echoing endless music and here comes the devil. The devil has me fixed firm to the ground with pins and stakes in me, and the devil is towering over me, the devil is repeating, every time he announces himself as the devil he says, the devil does this, he talks of himself in the third person like average assholes everywhere, is my first impression of the devil, I'm afraid, and also that he is not red, not scarlet, but alchemical black and gold.

And also huge, and towering, the devil towers, is what he is saying to himself, the devil looms, but that might be just taking advantage of my prone position on the ground. Finally I manage to pluck out all of the swords that are pinning me to the ground so that I can wrestle with this devil, the devil wrestles, he informs me, though I knew that already, and then he transforms into a nurse, who is telling me I have to get back into my bed, and it's like I am in a hospital ward, and these swords are tubes, feeding my body, and at one point a doctor with a clipboard appears and asks me what it is that I did, he says to me, what was it that you used to do, and I tell him, used to, what do you mean, used to, Adam is the greatest fighter, is what I say to him, now I am speaking as the devil, and he says to me, you will never fight again, he says, and then this music comes back in, this atomic music, and the girl who called me a male chauvinist pig is by my side and her name is Madini, she tells me, and the devil is vanquished, for now, although I know he is waiting for me, out there, up ahead, this is what makes me the greatest fighter, I tell Madini, that I am ready for the devil, and I head back home on my own, where the blond German is collapsed on the floor after concussing himself with the grill pan on the cooker trying to make toast while inebriated.

SUZY

Under the awning, by the VW bus at night, this is Romania, and there are sounds of wild dogs all around. Alan is perturbed but you tell him not to worry, they will circle the light, you say, but they won't step into it. A blackened kettle suspended above a campfire lets out a high whistle. And then a black dog – suddenly! – there is the appearance of this black dog, and it bounds into the light. It breaks the circle and bares its ferocious teeth, this great black dog with eyes and teeth come out of the night. And it goes for Alan. Alan stumbles backwards and tries to kick it, but it gets its jaws around Alan's leg and now it is dragging him, this great black dog is dragging Alan into the dark beyond the light, and that's when you rise up, you rise up and you reach for the kettle that is boiling, and you swing it through the air and you bring it down on this great fucking black dog that has Alan in its power, and it instantly retreats, but not before you empty the entire damn thing over its head, so that this great beast is howling in terror and is literally dissolving, back into the dark, and the night, as you walk towards it with your arms raised as if banishing a demon.

And that is when the second miracle occurs. There is a single
light suspended in the darkness, a tiny pin-point of light as
at the end of a tunnel, or at the bottom of a well, and it starts
to expand, slowly, like the arrival of a distant star, until it is
no longer a star but the eye of a great cyclops, approaching,
from out of the dark, and now it is a second terror come out
of the night, a figure in a spacesuit, with a full body-suit,
like armour, and with a respiratory device that covers its
face, and but then it spoke; got any whisky, it said. That
wound looks serious, it said. Alan lay there, in pain and in
terror, while you calmly replied that, yes, you did indeed
have a single malt in the van, believing that the stranger
was some kind of otherworldly surgeon sent in recompense
for the banishing of the black dog, and believing, further,
that it intended to sterilise the wound with the alcohol before
operating on it with who knows what kind of science-fiction
scalpel, but instead the thing took a seat on a nearby tree
stump and requested two glasses, while addressing you as
darling, and now you, too, are a little scared and discomfited,
after all, anything could happen, and all the while Alan is on
the floor in agony, and now that you are able to look closer
you can see that this stranger's outfit looks less futuristic
than just plain down-and-out, it looks more like he is wearing
black plastic bin bags, actually, and a pair of goggles, and
some kind of old military respirator, in other words he is
straight out of your worst dreams, like a Victorian serial
killer, and then when he had you raise a glass with him
he said, here's to close shaves, and it was hard to suppress
a shudder when he said that, but even worse was when
this terrible stranger took his goggles off and had you look
straight into his eyes, look at me, he said, look at me, and
you looked into his eyes right then and what you saw there
made you weep, it made you break down crying right there
in the night, the content of this outlandish stranger's eyes
was enough to break you, even after you had cast out that

dog, and then the stranger put his goggles back on, and rose, or floated, was what it felt like – there was soft birdsong as he went, soft birdsong in the night – and as he approached Alan, who was writhing on the floor in pain and in terror, he reached up into the night and brought down a tiny plumed bird, a bird of impossibly reflective black feathers, and he introduced it to the wound in Alan's leg, and it disappeared inside him with a song, and when you both woke there was no mark or scar like in a dream come true even though your VW bus had been stolen and all your belongings lay around you in a deliberate circle.

After that, you hitchhiked your way into Ukraine, and next to Georgia, where the sound of distant dogs woke you in a terror in the night.

4. THE EMPEROR

ADAM

I went for a walk in the forest, in the middle of Prague,
a dark forest like in a vampire novel; I was walking with
Madini. She asked me what I was doing here, in Prague, and
I told her at first I just came here because it was better than
East Berlin and plus I had been introduced to one of the big
men here who could give me a job and lodgings. Lodgings, I
said to Madini, where did that word come from, I never used
that word before, and Madini said to me, I think, rather, you
are writing a book, and I assured her, no, no, I did not travel
to Prague to write my novel like some beatnik, and I told her
I was more physical than that, and that I didn't just live in
my head, and she said to me, are you sure?

We arrived at her apartment, which must have been on
the edge of the forest. In her apartment there were glass
bookshelves with old books on them. You really read those old
books? I asked her and she told me that she read new books,
as well, and I told her, well, you won't be reading my new one
in a hurry, and again she just said, are you sure?

I told her I had a fight coming up against some young guy
calling himself The Amalgamator. What kind of a name is
that, I said to her, and she said to me, in metallurgy it is the
name of the process of the mixing of Mercury. I thought it
was a name for a machine that counts money.

SUZY

In Kandahar you attract a lot of unwelcome attention. Alan
has come here to visit some poet friend who lives part-time in
the cave of his guru, a cave in the shape of a skull, they say,

somewhere in the desert outside the city. In the meantime, you rent a one-bedroom apartment with a rickety fire escape and a balcony that overlooks a market where there are butchered animal carcasses laid out on tables draped with white sheets, this mud-covered market that has graffiti on the wall that shows a syringe going into a brain and the slogan 'Feed Your Head', and you and Alan eat at the market, most days, in a bombed-out little brick shelter where Alan makes sure they char the lamb till it's black and that they wash the salad with boiling water, but even then it takes weeks before he'll try it, this washed salad of tomatoes and red onion, that is delicious, actually, and you wished he wasn't quite so fearful about stuff like that.

Alan buys a tasselled leather pouch from a stall and gets talking to the guy who makes them. Alan asks him if there is anywhere he can score hash but this guy says, my friend, I can get you much better shit than that, he says, I can get you virgin snow, is what he calls it, and what he means is top-quality, totally pure, uncut Afghan heroin. Of course, you try it first, and when you not only survive, but declare it to be the Best, Fuck, Ever, then Alan shoots up, too, and you lie there, in each other's arms, on this messed-up bed, overlooking this filthy market and you repeat, beneath your breath, you say, yes, forever, yes, forever.

There is a girl in the market you have taken a shine to. But it's the men you have to watch. They grab their balls and mime ass-fucking you even when you are with Alan; blatantly. A tall aristocratic blonde in a mini-dress, oversized sunglasses and a floppy hat is a sight to see. Your neighbours are watching you through a crack in the door. There is whispering at night, and movement, outside, on the fire escape. Then one morning you find an empty birdcage, left there by who knows what or why, a single empty birdcage rusting in the sun. Alan says that if you rigged up an old turntable and cut out some material you could make a birdcage into a dream machine. He says he will drop it by a guy he knows in the café to help him modify it. But of course you both thought about that bird that was inside him, or was it, and how it might yet work its way out.

THE • HIEROPHANT

5. THE HIEROPHANT

ADAM

The Amalgamator's theme song is called 'Band of Gold';
mine is Frank Zappa. The Amalgamator is a young black
Czechoslovakian and I know the young ones are dangerous,
they are so fast. The referee asks us if we know the rules
and I am so much on speed I just say, yes, yes! I am eager
to get on and destroy this guy. I am eager to send him
somewhere he has no name. I can't see the crowd but I can
hear the Germans who are instructing me to dispatch this
guy the same way he came, up his mother's hole. Then I see
Coy, Coy is in my corner, I'll be your cut man, he is saying,
and he's saying, no playing the long game. Take him out of
the game early, he is saying, he'll try to wear you down, so
make every punch count. The Amalgamator crosses himself
and kisses his gloves and points to the ceiling with respect.
Then he looks at me like with a big cat's eyes from out of the
safety of the forest, reading my body, and then he smiles,
as if he has realised where I am best pregnable, like now he
knows just exactly how the night will pan out, and they ring
the bell and he comes out with his shoulders hunched, as
if to make his silhouette more frightening, and it's true he
looks like a black monk or a great black bird in silhouette,
and my legs are aching already in this fight, why are my
legs aching already, and he gets me on the ropes but the
upper cuts are getting nowhere, and I manage to bat one off
at the same time as I drive a jab straight into his fat face
that ripples in slow motion, the fat on his face ripples like
waves into water, and I'm not done yet, I skip back, and to
the right, and cuff him with a right hook that is more about
breaking the skin than impact, but now he is bleeding, he
is bleeding from a gash in his eyebrow, and I feel myself
circling him, now, only this time as the big cat in the

bleeding desert, and I hear a word, where did it come from, The Amalgamator, the audience, Coy the cut man in my corner, but the word is: Adam. Someone is calling my name like it is out of the past, and I wonder if it's all the dead I left behind, in East Germany, speaking, the living dead in jails, pleading: Adam!

The Amalgamator's cut man has Vaseline on the cut, and we're back in the game, but now all I can see is an exit wound, just above his right eye. He ducks, bounces, I miss him by centimetres, but I'm off balance, and I fall into his arms, and he holds me, and I can smell him, a damp changing room in hell, and already I am doing those exhausted short-range rabbit punches that I should be falling back on in round nine and it's only still the end of the first.

I go back to my corner and Madini is there with my cut man, Coy, and she is wearing a T-shirt with my name on it, and there is a little star. She says to me, unsound him, she says, and for a second I doubt myself; have I the right? And the battle pauses, and then I realise there is nothing to be thought through, that the gift of my fist down his throat was exactly what was needed to deliver this clown to the future, that the trick is to fight like brothers, and so I bear down on the bastard, I leer at him with my mouthguard all foaming with saliva, and I drive my fist straight into the little cut on his eyebrow as his forehead bursts open and the two of us are showered with blood before it's all over, and The Amalgamator's team, whose cut man I didn't realise was actually his old dad, throw in the towel.

Afterwards I saw a dildo for the first time because Madini had bought us one to treat us, but I couldn't have sex because I was so hyped up and gibbering on speed that I felt inadequate and I said, it looks kind of big, is that really the

size of an average male member, as I watched her giving
herself an orgasm instead, and the next day when I came
back from doing the rounds with Coy and leaning on clowns,
the Germans and the Ethiopian had stuck empty egg cartons
to the walls of my bedroom as a joke about how loud we were.

SUZY

You make the connection with the Greek poet, the Greek poet
who, it turns out, lived for a while in Deià, on the island of
Mallorca. At the same time as Christopher Perret? Alan asks
him. The same time in the mid-sixties when Perret was living
there and drinking wine on the mountaintops and writing
poetry to his lover, Anne, with titles like 'Daybreak' and
'Etched in Snow' and 'Blood' and 'Sunrise of a Flower' and
'Virgin My Bride' and 'Tomorrow' and 'Bird (for Anne)' and
'Night' and 'Elegy for the Golden Bird'? And this Greek poet
(what was his name, Vasilis, Basilic?) confirmed that yes, he
had seen Christopher on the island, shortly before his tragic
death, but then he pooh-poohed his poetry, saying he was
a minor talent, that it was adolescent love poetry, nothing
more, as if that didn't have just as much love and feeling and
freshness and vitality and eternity to it as some old world-
weary Greek bloke dropping random non-sequiturs like a
fridge magnet, is what his poetry reads like, in my opinion,
I'm sorry, but who cares about his poetry anyway, Alan
said, later, after the two of you had been driven back to your
apartment, and while you were changing to go to this new
teashop that Basilic has recommended you, a place where
expat poets and hoodlums and artists drank mint tea in the
sunshine and smoked kif, and shot up, too, while you were
getting ready Alan shrugged and admitted who cares about
his poetry, I mean, this guy lives part-time in the eye socket
of a stone skull in the desert in Afghanistan where his guru
is meditating 24/7, a guru that received a vision informing

him that he was the only thing standing between absolute universal entropy and the world going along as it is, and that what he was going to have to do is walk through the desert and find a great stone skull and then sleep in its eye and pray constantly in order to hold off the end of the world; this is a guy who has nothing more to prove about poetry, Alan said.

THE • LOVERS

6. THE LOVERS

ADAM

Then we went to a snooker club in Prague. And I thought I
lost my mind. I thought it was a morgue. I freaked out halfway
through the game. I could see off into the distance and it was
like the tables were laid out forever, the green tables lit up by
strip lights, the dark velvet interior, the players like assistants
or psychopomps, what is that word psychopomp doing here,
exactly, I am in a morgue, I am telling the Germans, this
morgue goes on forever, I am saying, and the Germans are
saying, calm down, man, calm down, they are saying, this is a
snooker hall, not a morgue, they're saying, you need to go easy
on the whizz, is what they are saying, you are making yourself
paranoid, they are saying, and I go outside, I am so bugged I go
outside, and I am having palpitations at this point, I can feel
my heart in turmoil, and I'm so warm, it's so warm, this heat
is killing me, so that I ask a random girl, I'm sorry, I say, but
I have taken too much amphetamine and I am too hot, could
you please lick my forehead? And the unbelievable thing is, she
does it, she agrees to lick my forehead, she can see I am in some
distress, and she takes her cool tongue, and curls it all the way
over my forehead and it is such heaven, her cold touch, and
then she walks off, and I think to myself, all you have to do is
ask. Then I ran at top speed around the block about five times.

I started at a new gym because we had to cripple the owner of
the old one. I was sceptical at first because the guy who ran the
new gym had taken a brain haemorrhage but was somehow back
at it. I hate that word – that curse word – unspellable – please,
stay that way; damn haemorrhage. I hate it, yet here he was,
back training, when they said he would never walk and talk
again. Plus they called him The Claw, because of the way he
would draw opponents in, and then crush them. The story was

that when he had his – awful word – that his physiotherapist
told him he would never fight again. And The Claw handed him
a handwritten note, written, presumably, with his one good
hand – his final claw – that said, I don't allow negative people
in my life get the fuck out. And here he was, back training, only
he used these floppy racket-type things and not pads, because
he had no sensation in one arm, so God knows how he even
remembered to stand up, never mind dance around the ring like
a show-off, although the rumour was that he only had feeling left
in one bollock, and just part of his arsehole, as well.

That's when everything changed. Coy was still my mentor,
and now he was my manager, too; but The Claw became my
inspiration. I watched the way he danced around the ring like a
show-off. How nobody would suspect he was half paralysed. And
I told myself. It is there for the asking. Nobody will suspect. I
was starting to put things together. I was starting to feel directed
ever since I had come to this Prague. I realised my destiny was
to be a fighter. I started entering amateur competitions, and I was
destroying everyone. For me the fights were like black holes. I
went into blackout mode as soon as the bell went and I woke up
towering over the crumpled, convulsing bodies, of kids, really,
because one kid took convulsions after I knocked him down and I
thought I might have my first death on my hands this early, but no.

SUZY

You start to spend more time with the girl in the market. During
the day Alan is off making connections and smoking heroin. You
walk the market and compare the differences in your lives. I
come from a very well-off background, Suzy tells the girl, whose
name is Aifa, I never had to worry about money, which is one
good thing, she is saying to her, and that's why you came to
Afghanistan, Aifa asks her, you were looking for a misfortune?
Ha, that's one way of putting it, Suzy says, for adventure, for

danger, she explains. Just then a man makes a foul comment right in her ear. Let's go sit in the park, Suzy says. In the park there is a beautiful fountain. Children are running into – and leaping out of – this beautiful fountain in the park. My mother has a nature reserve in the mountains, Aifa tells her. My husband won't let me go. You can go, though, if you would like to, Aifa says, my mother is always looking for helpers to work for her. She looks after orphan animals there, she says, and grows all sorts of food, and flowers. It is really wonderful there.

You take out your flask, a beautiful old copper flask; where did you find it? The top breaks down into two delightful thimbles that you fill with hot peppermint tea. I feel an increasing urge to get lost, Suzy tells Aifa, and all Aifa says is, it is in the mountains, that is all she says, and Suzy imagines an elevated fairyland of green plateaus and beautiful fountains strung between perilous mountaintops and Suzy working alongside her mother in perfect peace.

Alan is excited to be in Afghanistan. He says you can see yourself more clearly here, though the word he actually uses is 'starkly'. He writes home: 'send poetry/have press'. The poems arrive and Alan starts printing them in the basement of this café, this expat bar filled with headcases and poets and mad bandits; the Kandahar Broadsides. Alan and whatever this actual Greek poet's fucking name is are making plans to hike to this stone skull where his guru maintains the world in a sacred trance. One day, while out walking alone, you are accosted by a young man who calls you a cunt-lapping whore and who warns you to stay away from his sister. You don't mention this to Alan, who is chasing heroin with pipes of mad Afghani hash while printing all of this shit in this café basement like it's the end of the world. You are falling out of love with Alan so soon. His writing and printing and his ceaseless making connections. His basic inability to be.

THE · CHARIOT

7. THE CHARIOT

ADAM

My first big fight was with a gangster name of Rico 'Iron Man' Martini. I hadn't had sex in months. The Claw insisted that I build up my sperm to the point that my balls were bursting in order to kill this guy, though he may just have been punishing me for his own busted nuts. And there's Madini in the front row wearing a little hot-pants suit. Good grief. Fighting made me really horny. When I would leave the gym I would walk down the road imagining taking every good-looking woman and bending her over a hedge. But then the amphetamine countered it. Some people can go all night on the stuff, but for me it was hopeless.

The fights are taking place at the halls of the university. There are a bunch of cards. We're the last fight before the interval. The Claw can't get up the stairs. He can dance around the ring like a show-off, but he can't climb a flight of stairs. So he insists on getting this mobility lift up these ten steps or so. And of course Martini's crew rock up right then, and they see my trainer, on a mobility lift to avoid ten stairs, and he sees them, and he says, alright boys, he says, you look like a bunch of midgets from up here, he says, all the time rising about one mile an hour into the air, and Coy bounds up the steps and he opens the lift for The Claw, and he bows, he bows in front of The Claw, who is now back on level ground and so can walk like he is perfectly normal, and you can see that Martini's team are freaked out as they enter the building, muttering among themselves and staring, who are these madmen, and The Claw puts his good arm or his bad arm around me, who knows which, and he says, it is possible to turn any situation to your advantage, he says, and as Coy's putting on my wraps I'm repeating it to myself like a mantra.

It is possible to turn any situation to your advantage. It is there for the asking. No one will ever suspect. These wraps that smell of sweat. I love the smell of sweat and of men's dressing rooms. I love the wild talk.

He tied her to a chair in a barber's shop that was closed for the night, someone says. Then he went out for a pizza. Did he bring her back a slice? his trainer asks him. Did he fuck, he says, in fact he ate in.

In the distance there is Hendrix, 'Purple Haze', some boxer's intro, amateur, he's up against someone playing 'Sympathy for the Devil' by The Rolling Stones and right away, I see that devil, I see that same devil I wrestled with, and I say to Coy, wait, don't put my gloves on yet, I want to run round the block, and The Claw says, what the fuck is the kid saying? Rather than just ask me directly he would direct these questions to Coy for some reason, and Coy said, he said he wants to quickly run around the block, and The Claw says, it's madness, tell him it's madness, and then he turns to me and he says, it's madness, what if you trip over a bit of upturned concrete or catch your ankle in a pothole on the street, but I say to him, what if I slip having a piss, I say, and then I add, live dangerously, I say, and The Claw's not about to contradict that, and so I run outside, it's early evening in Prague, and I take a little wrap of speed out of my shorts and I swallow it, and then I stand there, shadowboxing, as the sun goes down, orange, and impossibly large, in the past, on my big night long ago.

SUZY

Someone has nailed the corpse of a bat through its wings to your door in the shape of a nightmare. You tell Alan that we should move out, but he's getting ready for this fucking

pilgrimage he's going on to see this poet's guru, it's fine,
he says, don't worry, he says, I can get us a gun, he says, a
Mauser, from a taxi driver he knows, a fucking semi-automatic
handgun, a beautiful gun, but still, and they have the Greek
poet whatever the fuck his name is drive them out into the
desert, to this abandoned shanty town, where they set up tins
and plastic containers and practise with this semi-automatic,
and you are good, born to it, this fucking unknown Greek poet
says – that's when you take out a line of Coke cans at 100
yards – and Alan has brought some wine, and some heroin,
and some cured meats, and there is a little river that runs
through this abandoned village, this empty homestead, really,
and it is of such a curious blue, like the pupil of an eye, blue,
and the three of you sit with your feet in this glassy blue
water and pass the wine back and forth, and smoke a few
trails, and in the distance, on the very top of a hill, stood out
like perfect silhouettes, there is a tribe of people, it looks like,
migrating, in a straight line, against the horizon, and you get
an incredible feeling, like this is still the morning of the world,
this is still our morning, and we are still seeing with the first
eyes ever, that's what Alan said it was like, then, still seeing
with the first eyes ever, you all felt it, this distant movement
of human beings as it had always been, over time, this lighting
out is forever, and you lay your head on Alan's shoulder, his
soft hair like Chris Hillman's when he was in The Byrds, and
that smell of Alan's, and those eyes, of course, and you look
down into the water and you look back at Alan's eyes and you
see those same distant waters, that same glassy blue, so far
away, now, so untouchable, but then, as when the three of you
watched this line of migrating humans come from the very
morning of the world.

8. ADJUSTMENT

ADAM

But where am I now? Where am I remembering this from? Every time I look, I can't find me. It's the speed, I tell myself, it's the amphetamines. Where am I? My music comes on, 'Trouble Every Day'. I'm led into the ring by Coy and The Claw, each of whom has a hand resting on my shoulders. I can't find me, I say to The Claw, I can't find where I am talking from. And The Claw says, put your attention in the ring, he says, and from there, bring your attention back to where you are. I just did it, I said, and I can't find me. You are the ring, he says, and he lifts the ropes for me to step through. In the ring I tell myself, I have no head, I have no head, I cannot take a hit on the head because I am headless, I am telling myself, as I bounce up and down on my toes and stretch my shoulders, my gold boxing shorts. I am telling myself I am only arms and legs, fists and feet, and the lights come up, the golden lights eliminate the audience completely and silence it utterly, there is nothing beyond these ropes. Wasn't it Atlas, the greatest of fighters, who held the entire world on his shoulders? We get up close and I can tell there's a referee, but I can't see him, I daren't look to the side, I need to stare at this Iron Man like I want to evacuate his spic bastard eyeballs. And his breath, his breath is fucking tacos or something, this fucking Mexican, what the fuck is a Mexican doing in Czechoslovakia? I am applying all my hatred to him, this wetback spic bastard. But then I remember altitude. How these fucking spic wetback sons of roaches are training basically up in the clouds, in Mexico City you have to take aspirin to thin your blood just to climb the damn stairs, and so when they go to fight abroad it is like there is no resistance at all, and so they're faster and stronger and can float like angels.

I back off into my corner and I have true tunnel vision. I am looking down a well at this dead spic motherfucker spread-eagled in the filthy water and the discarded nappies and that fucking grey water these fucking narco bitches drink with their tortillas fresh out of stinking rivers. He moves towards me. I bounce around him. I have my eye on his right hand. He is holding it like he is cradling something there. He leads with his left, this is textbook shit, exploratory, gauging his reach, or is it? He is circling me with his left, and it's like some voodoo shit, some death cult shit, I know Mexico, he is moving round me and drawing shapes in the air, this is like a spider, and barely a human, this devious non-human Mexican son of a bitch is working magic on me and of course I realise that there is no ban against magic in boxing, you just have to deal with it, and I start punching holes in his attack, I start countering him, he enters my space with the left, I cut under him, and I punch a hole in his web, and then I think, the Iron Man, wait, is it more like soldering, is it like a force field, and I feel my arms go weak, my legs go weak, this is high magic, this is what the Mexicans do, and then he hits me, like a chicken hypnotised by a snake, he smacks me right on my third eye and it's squidgy, I feel it in my brain, where is it, I'm wobbling, I am teetering, I tell myself, and I hear the Germans screaming in the audience, the Ethiopian and Madini, too, hold in there, you can do it, motherfucker, bad ass motherfucker, let's do this, and keep talking, Madini says, what, keep talking, and I'm up, I'm back on my feet, but I can't feel my legs, and I look to The Claw, and without saying anything he knows, he knows what to say, and he says, you are a blind man now, and I know exactly what he means, because I have lost all feeling in my extremities, and so must guess at my own size. And so I estimate where my fist is, and where, exactly, this shit-eating spic lowlife pussy bitch will move, I read his body and mine, with my eyes closed, and he walks right into my right, I skewer him with it, and I realise I had estimated that he would be a little further away, so that I drive my fist through his head, aiming for a spot beyond, and now he has no legs or arms to rely on, and is just a helpless spic torso contorting on the floor. Only now he, too, is a blind man, and moves like a spider. Two blind men, in an illuminated dance, in the dark.

He's back on his feet. But he misjudges a right hook that throws him off balance. His shorts are tight. He has the beginnings of an erection. It turns me on. To fight a little spic bitch with a hard-on. What's so hot about your own destruction, I want to say, but there is no time for words, keep talking, and as he stumbles I simply drop my right, and bring it straight back up again, at an angle of 45 degrees, so that I lift him off his feet and send him through the air, so that when he lands the ring ripples, like a stone into water, and there's a blood bubble coming out of his nose and he's dead, I fucking killed him, the Iron Man is dead on his back from me, and in another world. That's when I have to flee the country.

SUZY

When you see a purple sunbird for the first time, you are overcome. You are visiting Aifa in disguise at the café where she works, and she has a purple sunbird there in a cage. It sings excitedly on its perch when you arrive. Is that a real bird, you ask her, because it is hard to believe, it appears to be flitting through colours in front of your eyes. I am a saviour of black birds, Aifa tells you, her English is precious, when they die I collect their feathers, she tells you, and she opens a deep drawer filled with feathers that dazzles like a black mirror or a blanket of bright ashes. It looks exactly like the bird that is inside Alan. It is colour that absorbs all light, Aifa tells you. Not a black mirror, you think, then. Rather, a black sun.

THE ·HERMIT

9. THE HERMIT

ADAM

Back then the easiest way to get to the West was to get
arrested and spend two years rotting in a cell before West
Germany would buy your freedom. This is what happened
to a friend of mine when his parents got arrested trying to
escape. But I told Coy, I don't have two years to rot in a cell
if I want to make it as a boxer, and Coy said, wait, let me
think about this, and then he said, okay, he said, I think
it can be easily done, I know a big man there, I will have a
gang buy us instead, they can forge the paperwork, it's not
a problem, I'm coming, he said, we will make our fortune
together, he said, but what about The Claw, I said to him,
and Coy said he would ask him, but The Claw said he didn't
want to be people-smuggled by a gang at this stage in the
game, especially with him being half paralysed, and he said,
that boy is going to do us all proud, he said to Coy, and then
he turned to me and he said, I'll see you on the telly, he said,
and then I thought he was going to cry but then he said, in
black and white, mind, and then he shook his head and he
walked off as if there was nothing wrong with him at all, and
that's the last time I saw The Claw in real life because this
gang came through with the money fast when they thought
they might be buying into a future superstar boxer's career,
which is how Coy had sold it, and so now, the pressure is on,
and Coy and I are on a train sat across from a know-all party
member, headed through Czechoslovakia for Berlin, lit up,
in the dark, a know-all party member who is debating with
himself on all sorts of issues because God knows Coy and I
were saying nothing.

Is Muhammad Ali really the greatest, he is saying, this
fatuous party man, dressed in a tan safari suit and with

ridiculous sideburns, because to my mind he spoke against
his country and you can't be great if you don't represent your
country, if you don't personify where you come from, you can't
be great, in my opinion. Here, where I am, is the greatest, is
what you are saying, because, after all, the greatest was born
from the greatest, it stands to reason, doesn't it, tautologies
stand to reason because they are self-evident statements of
what is, God is God, and what do you think of that, a man
like myself saying God's existence is self-evident, and in the
next breath I praise Tito, the greatest leader, in my opinion,
that communism has produced, and he went on like this as
Coy and I gazed out of the window, into the night, into the
dark forest, and I thought of Madini, and our sad farewell,
how she had said that I would find my own Madini, once
more, out there, and I thought, yes, but in black and white,
and not in colour, before the party man launched into another
self-directed tirade about the flower power, was what he said,
this flower power, he said, what they don't understand is that
flower power relies on sun power, on the flaming heart of the
destructive sun, he said, and he repeated it, power, power
of smelting, he said, it is the molten cores of these planets
that produce flowers, he said, and at what unimaginable
cost, which is what we, in the progressive world, have long
understood, that only the atomic reckoning of mankind with
its environment, with its collective shoulder to the wheel,
can generate enough fire and force to equal the life force
of flowers, otherwise we are mere botanists, cataloguing
our encounters with this overwhelming, unknown force of
creation, rather than personifying that very power ourselves,
in industry, and at this point Coy looked at me, and I looked
back at him, and I thought, thank fuck every speeding second
is taking us further from this kind of conversation for life.

SUZY

You make the decision to leave without telling Alan. Why?
The call to adventure? This search for what Aifa called a
misfortune? What was it you saw in the terrible eyes of that
stranger? A reflection, perhaps? It is inexplicable, this feeling
in your gut, in the pit of your lungs, that is now leading the
way. You think of your father, and all that you could have
been, all that you were supposed to be, as you prepare to
abandon this why forever. Aifa, you say, darling Aifa, I have
made the decision to walk into the mountains in order to
serve your mother in her garden, and perhaps one day you
can come to us, too, darling Aifa, she says, and Aifa warns
her to keep her voice down and then she says, I have made
you a headdress so that my mother may recognise you, and
she hands you a perfect halo of black bird feathers.

You return to your apartment and pack a rucksack. You walk
through the market in a daze; everything is illuminated,
now, now that you have decided to give it all away. Aifa's
directions were vague. Head for Senjaray, and then up, into
the mountains. My mother's name is Madini, she told you.
Her garden is on a beautiful mountain plane where animals
graze in idyllic peace, she said. And so you set out for this
garden high in the mountains. On the way out of town you
thumb down a ride from an older man in a dilapidated Land
Rover who tells you he is an author writing about the cuisine
of the area. These Afghans never stop eating, he marvels,
while stuffing some bolani into his mouth. His white shirt
is all dirty and covered with grease and he has an in-car
cassette player – wow – playing 'Something in the Air' by
Thunderclap Newman from somewhere across the event
horizon, it sounds like. He tells you he is on his way to a
'small kitchen' and asks if you would like to join him for a
meal, and then it emerges that you actually know each other

vaguely, impossibly, because it turns out his brother is the illustrator John Cooper, famous for his ahead-of-the-times sci-fi covers for authors like Asimov and Clarke as well as the magazines of the 'new wave' and that this is Simon Cooper, his gourmet brother, rich enough to be touring the mountains of Afghanistan in search of his own terms of misfortune, it occurs to you then, and of course your father worked for a publishing company that published Asimov and Ballard and so all of these connections come together, these tentacles, it almost feels like, as you drive into the mountains with Simon in search of this perfect dish.

But when you get to Senjaray it is awful, no one is happy to see you, the so-called restaurant is the garden of someone's house with stone walls in a rough part of town where passing locals leer over you and shout insults while you eat this sweet nut soup until someone throws this huge boulder over the wall and Simon suggests you get back into the Land Rover and make quick your escape and he drives half drunk, half drunk on this perfidious secret vegetable alcohol they have been plying you with, which they won't touch themselves, like fucking Buckfast monks, it occurs to me now, they won't go fucking near it, and further, into the mountains, where you park up at a crazy vantage point, where the moon illuminates the desert, and all of this vast terrain beneath your feet, so that it feels like it is frozen there, forever, you think, as you both climb into the back of the Land Rover and spoon and fall instantly asleep beneath the rugs and the throws and Simon doesn't even try to fire in: fixed, forever.

FORTUNE

10. FORTUNE

ADAM

This gang we sold ourselves to, you should've seen this gang.
They were revolutionary leftists. Coy and I couldn't believe
it. We thought we had seen the last of this kind of thing.
You'd think that us paying a gang to get us the hell out of the
Eastern Bloc might've alerted them to the miserable situation
there, but no, they were running rackets and protection
schemes and of course drug smuggling, from Afghanistan,
while funnelling money into revolutionary activity. You
should run a training camp, this guy says to me, me and Coy
are sat back in the boot of an estate car, laid out, actually,
there are rugs and cushions in there, these four goons had
met us at the airport, just to make sure their investment
didn't go AWOL, and the lead goon, who was wearing a
leather jacket with mirrored aviator shades and who was
bald at the top but who had long hair at the sides and whose
name was Spidey, says to me, you could teach unarmed
combat, and I said to him, I'm a boxer, not a street fighter,
and only but Coy corrects him and says, he started out as a
street fighter, my friends, he says, that would be going back
to his roots, whereas we must keep an eye on the future, my
friends, he said, don't you agree, wouldn't it mean more for
the cause to have a revolutionary world champion than to
teach a few goons how to wrestle on the floor, and the goons
nodded and said, yeah, man, think about it, they said. Spidey
passed a joint back to this clown with hair down to his ass
and he took a hit and he passed it back to me, and of course
Coy didn't smoke, and this clown with the hair whose name
was Crow said, you cool, man, he asked Coy, and Coy said,
I'm ice cold, he said, and for an instant the car fell silent, and
I felt proud of Coy, and tough, but then we were all so stoned
we forgot it had even happened and someone turned on the

radio and it was Jimi Hendrix, 'All Along the Watchtower', and we sailed off across the autobahn, straight into this huge setting sun and all of the billboards and advertisements and it was so bright, I remember it was so bright.

SUZY

The next morning you tell Simon about your quest for Aifa's mother, and for her garden, on a mountaintop, somewhere. The call to prayer echoes around the hills as you breakfast on spiced eggs and flatbread that Simon prepares over a gas burner in the open trunk of the car. You are still using heroin, in secret, but you're running low. I'm sorry to hear about your parents, Simon tells you, I had no idea. Mother died of a broken heart, you tell him, but you fail to mention your father. I left my boyfriend behind in Kandahar, you tell Simon. I don't know why I did it, you tell him. Then: the last time I ever saw Father was at the circus, you tell him. Yes, it was so strange. He had been ailing for some time and Mother called and said your father has a last burst of energy and he wants to see you and to do something together. Well, what does he want to do? I asked Mother. He wants to go to the circus, she said. He has never mentioned wanting to go to the circus before, I said, but Mother said, no, dear, your father has talked about taking you to the circus for the longest time. He just always presumed you would say no. I felt terrible then, how I had unwittingly stood in the way of Father's great desire for me, but then, that was typical of Father. I called to pick him up in my car and he shuffled out of the house like a dead man walking. His bones were jutting out, his skin was dark yellow, his beard old and grey. I helped him into the car and then we sat in silence and said nothing all the way to this Big Top they had erected in Hyde Park. Father couldn't drink any more so I left him on a bench while I got myself a large glass of wine. I could see him from the queue there, curled over like the worst question mark ever, his head in his hands the entire time. Then we went in. The lights dimmed and some kind of Mad Hatter figure or court jester bemoaned the falling of a kingdom, and the ceding of the crown. Then blamed it on a Thief of Fire. I looked at Father and he was as rapt as any dying man could be. Then some clowns bounced on sticks. Wow, it was pretty good. Then a guy who looked like a Samoan lay down in a sheet of flames and wasn't even consumed. Okay, wow again. Then came the most spectacular of all. An impossibly beautiful young man, who looked like a blaggard Romanian Romeo pirate in a string vest and tight leather trousers and with one nipple showing, wrapped some long fabrics around his wrists and ascended into the air. Wow. Yes, wow again. And then this woman appears, this girl, this beautiful woman. Her age is impossible to ascertain. And she, too, is lifted into the air with the aid of wraps. And they dance, in the air, right there in the air above Father and me, they swivel around above our heads, and they increase in speed before – suddenly! – the girl undoes her wraps and leaps through the air onto the torso of her man and he takes her and he throws her over his shoulder and passes her all the way around him – at one point she is clinging to his feet! – before righting her, once more, in his arms . . . I was sure father was crying, also, though I didn't dare look. Who knows what happened after that. On the way back home, which was our last conversation ever, I asked Father which act he had liked best and all he said was: The Lovers. I think that's why I did it, you told Simon Cooper, that morning, who knows?

II. LUST

ADAM

We came to a long, empty street that looked derelict. By this time it was dark. There was a single window lit up, on the top floor of this apartment block. There was music coming from it, loud rock music, hypnotic loud rock music. Someone was singing about flowers dying. All flowers must die, they were singing, to this hypnotic rhythm. This is where you will be staying, Spidey said to us, and he pointed up at the window, which at this point had the silhouette of someone with long hair nodding their head slowly in time to this endless music. Do they intend to play all night? Coy asked Spidey and Spidey said, sometimes all day and all night, he said, and he shrugged, and then he said that – give me a break – night-time is a bourgeois construct, he said, night-time is the time of desire, was what he said, and of its liberation, the night is not appointed as recovery time for work, he said, and he pointed back up at the band, jamming, lit up through a window in the dark, this isn't slave labour, he said, these are free men, he said, and I said to him, what is the night-time appointed for, but he didn't hear me and just walked into the building and I followed him up each flight of stairs until we came to the very top, which was like an L-shaped warehouse studio and the band were set up jamming beneath a glass ceiling and there were plants hanging down and low beds with throws on them, and low tables with incense burning, and there were hammocks strung across various alcoves and candles burning, and the band played 'Presence of the Lord' by Blind Faith, which I didn't know at the time was destined to become my new theme song. I was exhausted, and Coy and I clambered into two hammocks, strung up around the corner from the band, and fell asleep.

SUZY

Simon agrees to accompany you on your trek to find this mythic
mountain garden of Madini. Why not, he says, good-naturedly,
why not, after all, it could all be fodder for the book, if she has
some unlikely Edenic vegetable garden in the mountains. In the
meantime he is meeting with a guide in the next village who
he has paid to source good food spots, or what Simon insists on
calling 'quality grub locales'. This guy is a legend, Simon warns
you. He is an itinerant hippy known as Boz. Boz? Boz. When
you see him he is wearing hateful flip-flops and is dressed
like the worst surfer ever. Boz, my man, how is it hanging?
is how Simon greets him. You just give a sort of disdainful
wave. High as the sky, my brother, Boz greets him, high as the
motherfucking sky. Then they high-five and shoulder wrestle.
And who's the little lady? Boz asks Simon. I'm a woman named
Suzy, to you, you reply, but Boz just flaps his right hand like
he's trying to put out the flames and lets out a slow inhale.
Looks like we got a live one, he says. All you can do is roll your
eyes. My dudes, he says, my lord and my lady of the royal court,
he says, do I have one motherfucking itinerary for you. First
up, right where we stand, do you see that hole-in-the-wall gaff
there (he is literally pointing to a crack in a wall that it looks
like a fucking emu has pissed over), inside that admittedly
primitive entrance way, you are about to have some of the best
chicken kebabs of your ever-loving lives, though they don't call
it kebabs, here they call it shashlik. You follow him through
this strange erotic vulva entrance, it occurs to you, and in the
room there is a single mad butcher who has the corpses of five
chickens partially plucked and hanging from a wire across
the ceiling. Boz greets him with an upraised high-five but the
butcher just grunts and doesn't even take the roll-up out of his
mouth. Rahim, my man, looking good, my brother, Boz says, to
no avail, but right then an old woman in black robes comes out
and encourages you to sit and then she points to a little screen

in the corner, is that a TV, and she switches it on, and she lights some candles, and she disappears, and your man Rahim pours you all a shot of something that is green like absinthe and he starts chopping these chicken carcasses right in front of you, Simon is in his element, well played, my main man, he is praising Boz's skills in scouting quality grub locales that are as authentic as fuck, and then this TV kicks into life, this small black-and-white screen, really, more like a primitive security camera; and a woman is dancing. A long-haired woman is dancing in what looks like a sparsely dressed bedroom wearing nothing but a bikini in black and white and in slow motion. What is this? you ask Boz. Where is this? Is this live? We don't want to see this, you say to him. Boz asks your man Rahim what's the script with the chick, but all Rahim says is 'film'. Is that live? you ask him. Is someone dancing here, somewhere? you ask him. But all he repeats is 'film'. Film, for you, he says, and he points to you all and shrugs. The dancing is lacklustre, it has to be said. But still, there is something about it. I don't know if they want to watch this, Rahim, my good buddy, Boz says, I just don't think it's to their taste, man, he says, and he makes a secret sign that he thinks you cannot see, indicating that you are some kind of mental feminist killjoy, it looks like, but your man Rahim ignores him and instead addresses Simon. You don't like women? he asks him. No, it's not that, Simon says. I love women, I think they're great, he says. Good, your man Rahim says, and he goes back to flipping these chicken pieces that, it has to be said, smell completely fucking amazing, and this spice mix, and this combination of citrus and yogurt, and the sharp smoke in the room, and this booze that is going to your head already, and this lacklustre dancer, alive somewhere, and performing right now, is as if everything is speaking, everything is pleading for lack of love, *save me from lack of love*, the lacklustre dancer is pleading – the poor chickens, gored for some rich diversion, seem to intimate the same – even as it smells *so good*, even as it's *so enticing*.

12. THE HANGED MAN

ADAM

I remember trying to wake up. I remember trying to wake up and seeing the room exactly as it was, the band were packing away their guitars, the incense smoke in the air, the sound of bells, tinkling, and it was like I couldn't click back into my body, like I was just slightly out of sync, and I was trying to writhe myself from side to side, but I was paralysed, I could see Coy asleep, just across from me, the drool running down his chin, though I don't think I could smell his rotten breath, I had sight and sound, but not smell and touch, was how it felt, and then I realised there was a demon squatting on my chest, and holding me down, immobile, and I screamed harder, even though I had no voice, and I tossed from side to side, even though I had no feeling, just sight and sound so as no one else could see this demon that had me paralysed and in a terror not to move, and it was curled up there, like a stone cat, with a terrible grin, and I knew what its name was, and that I might be in hell, and I thought about what Madini had said about how I would find her everywhere.

But then I woke up and it was wake-and-bake time and I just thought, it was a contact high, that's what explains it, the air was thick with dope fumes, and I got stoned all over again, and Coy did too, as soon as we woke, what the hell, my friend, he said, after all, he said, this is the dawning of a new era, and he got toasted, and after lunch, which was the kind of prison gruel wardens pissed in, back in the East, standard-issue watery vegetarian slop, after Coy went back to sleep, I jumped on the back of a motorcycle with Crow, who took me to where I could buy a pair of Levi's and a leather jacket and some motorcycle boots only I was so high, I held him round the waist, instead of holding onto the bar behind me, but honestly it felt so good, like I was finally getting my physical sense of feeling back after that nightmare of sight and sound only.

SUZY

Of course you despaired. Of course you cried out in your mind what am I doing here, what is this massive folly? At times. But there were just as many other times when you were truly free of those whats, and those endless whys, and so it seemed possible to banish them forever, sometimes. But now you're not feeling well, and you need to score some junk. You have to ask Boz, you have to confess. It has put you in a position with that dreadful surfer hippy that you would rather not be in, but needs must, your stomach cramps are killing you, and you are no longer menstruating. I can score snow, Boz calls it, he calls it snow in all this desert. Sure, I can score snow, Duchess, and you let him call you that, for now. You have stopped off at an abandoned desert fortress that Simon has asked to see. You can hear their conversation from the back of the Land Rover where you lie covered in blankets and rugs. You hear Boz tell Simon how you are 'feeling unwell' and how we should press on to our next assignation; is he really so discreet?

Tonight Boz has arranged for some local chefs to cook for you at a guest house in the mountains. The guest house is part of a compound of houses surrounded by high stone walls and with large wooden gates leading in and out. Men lead camels past you as you cross the drawbridge. There is a smell of burning in the air. Your skin is crawling. Are you alright back there? Simon calls out. If you're nauseous I have a little hash you could smoke that might help? Is it the connection with your father that prevents you from being honest? No, you say, it's travel sickness, it will pass. Leave me in the van, you tell them, I need to sleep, you say. The thought of food disgusts you. I'll come back for you as soon as I can, Duchess, Boz says, and you nod, in trust, and you curl up like a foetus and dream of a man on a high trapeze and wake to Boz tying your arm, he has clean works with him and he is tying your arm and shooting you up, what an angel, BOZ.

13. DEATH

ADAM

Then he took me to an underground record shop. I got a tab
in here, Crow said, we can score some vinyl and take it back
to the pad, he said. Over the front of the underground record
shop there was a multi-coloured painting of an American
Indian called Kicking Bear who the shop was named after.
I had never seen so many records in my life. You into
psychedelic rock, man? Crow asked me and I said, sure, I
said, sure, I dig The Mothers, I said, and he said to me, what
about the Floyd, man? I told him I didn't know about the
Floyd, that on the other side of the curtain the sixties were
happening in secret, and he said, come the revolution, man,
there will be guitars in the streets, and he pulled out a record
called *Ummagumma* that on the sleeve had an image of the
band that was infinitely regressing, a mirror, inside a mirror,
inside a mirror that led to forever. Heavy, innit? Crow said.
Stick it on my tab, he said, and we'll jam it tonight. Back
at the pad the band were back jamming. Some girls were
dancing in the sunshine coming through the glass roof. I saw
Coy laid out on a beanbag talking to a guy with an eyepatch.
It felt so humid and warm in there. I was so stoned. The room
is breathing, I thought, everything is alive. I don't know why
I hadn't thought of that before, that everything is alive. But it
was uncanny. I wanted it more than ever now. Alive.

SUZY

I have been reading the most incredible manuscript, Simon
reveals the next morning at breakfast, a history of the
American Indian nation called *Bury My Heart at Wounded
Knee*, by one Dee Brown. It has really got me thinking, he
says. Out here in Afghanistan, it occurs to me, what we are

seeing is a form of Universal Indian. By which I mean a people with a relationship to the earth, and the sky, which is reverential. And which sees the animals, and plants, as gifts, to be tended, but also gods, to be worshipped. Plus, the idea of passing through. Wow, I need to read this book, you think to yourself, that is you completely, or as close as we've come, you think; a Universal Indian, passing through. They would undertake vision quests, Simon says. What is a vision quest? It is a journey in search of a sign. A sign? Like a bird, or an animal? A bird or an animal or the Earth itself in which the gods have come down. This is kin, you realise. You have come to recognise yourself. This is kin.

14. ART

ADAM

Pony was this guy who always wore a set of headphones on
his head, even though they weren't plugged into anything.
Plus he was always on a mission. He claimed he had cured
himself of mental illness. He said the doctors were hopeless.
That he was ready to die. That he had rehearsed it. He had
bought a bunch of disposable barbecues and had set them on
fire inside his car to see how long it took to fill with smoke,
only but he leapt out after about three minutes and burned
his car to the ground, which, considering he was completely
broke, was a complete disaster, and yet but it was the
absurdity of it, he claimed, that had cured him of mental
illness. And now he was back from the dead. Now he had the
calling of a mission, he said. Though what the mission was
wasn't clear. I would say to him, where are you off to? This is
when I would spot him charging past the Brandenburg Gate
in the rain and he would just say, *mission*, that was all. And
of course with his headphones on, and with the jack tucked
into his mad motorcycle jacket as usual.

Pony became my trainer, replacing The Claw, though not in
my heart, not quite yet, at least. It was his sense of mission,
Coy said, that convinced him. We were putting together
our team and Coy said, we need someone who believes in
destiny, he said. We need someone who believes in God-
given right, he insisted. We need someone with the balls
to take it for theirs, he maintained. Wait, Coy said, let me
think about this for a minute. Then he said, what about
your man on a mission? What about that guy Pony who lives
downstairs with the silent headphones on? With the silent
headphones on, I said to Coy, he should be in the loony bin, I
said, with that get-up on. We just sold ourselves to a gang of

international people traffickers in order to be in servitude to them for life, Coy reminded me, just so we could realise our dreams, he underlined. Who's crazy now? he said. We need true believers, Coy said, this is as serious as your life, he reminded me, and I said, okay, let's trust the loonies, at this point I am all for it. But can he even fight? I said to Coy. He cured himself of mental illness by burning down his own car, Coy reminded me, of course this guy can fight. And so we got him on board, and I have to admit, it was a genius move, in the end.

Because although he couldn't fight to save his life, he could describe a fight perfectly. He could comment on a fight and point out all sorts of things that you would never have noticed yourself. We would go to this gym that was on the top two floors of a rundown apartment building in Tiergarten and watch the amateur fights, in this madhouse where people would be fighting in cages and mass training sessions would be taking place – it was intense – and Pony would sit there, with his headphones on, he said it helped him concentrate, to block out all of the noise, and he would run these commentaries on the fights, and it was then that I began to realise that it was possible to read the future in the movement of a body. It's like chess, Pony explained, it's as mental as that. You must learn to read the bodies of other people, Pony said, and I said to him, but can you read your own body, and he said, no, that's the one thing you can't read. Like, for instance, he said, I couldn't read in my own body that I was going to fail in my suicide attempt, he said, but as for here, he said, and he pointed to a young Chinese guy who was on the ropes, taking body shot after body shot, he is drawing the attention down, he said, watch, he said, his opponent believes that he is tired out enough that he can focus on the body, and he forgets, he is there in the body completely, and he forgets the head, which is where the

Chinese will get him, he said, he has lost full-body awareness through the illusion of a simple triumph, and that is how the Chinese is playing it, do you see, Pony said, and I thought, is it possible, is it possible to be full-body conscious, and I tried to, I tried to feel my body right then, but there was no overall feeling, I can't feel my body, I thought, and I almost panicked, I can't feel my body all at once, and then I thought, who can, who can feel their bodies all at once, isn't it just a sensation here, a sensation there? Then the goal of the greatest fighter must be to experience their body in its totality, to know their body, as they themselves, completely. And I began to wonder if the real world, the material world, was more the domain of the saints than any heavenly ghost realm. And that it was in the ring where we are offered, body to body, the entrance to this realm, through the reading of the body of our opponents, was what Pony said, and it blew my mind. And in sex, too, I said to Pony, is where you find your body, but he just sat there with his headphones on in silence, like he was tuned to another wavelength entirely, as the Chinese took the head off his nameless opponent, in revenge, because he had forgotten it was even there.

SUZY

Yes, I think I have heard of this garden, Abdul-Ali tells you. It is an impossible garden tended by a blind woman, he says. Aifa didn't mention anything about Madini being blind. Nevertheless, Boz has introduced you to this renowned local guide who knows the area better than anyone, he says. Still, he has never found this garden. I've heard of it, he reiterates, but I have never found it. Why? he asks the party. Why do you think that might be? No one is any the wiser. Because, Abdul-Ali says, duh, because perhaps I am just not pure of heart enough, in order to see this wonderful garden, is the point. But even the woman that tends it can't see the garden, you go to say, but then you think better of it. He's saying it is some kind of metaphor, he is saying this garden is inside every one of us, you have heard this claptrap before, but this is a real garden, in real mountains, tended by the real mother of Aifa. But then Abdul-Ali says, I tell you what, I am willing to bet this garden can be found beyond the Cinvat Pass. Yes, I'd almost stake my life on it. The Cinvat Pass, Boz repeats, yeah, man, makes sense, man, there are supposed to be all these, like, weird communities out there, over this terrific pass, in the mountains, Boz explains for the benefit of the rest of us, all these fucking weird tribes lost to the world . . . if you want we can take a diversion, he says to Simon, take this cuisine thing way off the map, and he fist bumps him. Think about it, he says. Boz is so keen. BOZ.

THE·DEVIL

15. THE DEVIL

ADAM

There were a group of women who hung out in the building
that everyone called the old ladies. One night there was a
jazz show on the top floor, some musicians had come from
Wuppertal, it was free jazz, was what they called it. I had
heard a little bit through getting into The Mothers, like
Eric Dolphy, but nothing could prepare you for what they
sounded like. It was a bassist, a drummer and a saxophonist
with a walrus moustache. They played this screaming
ferocious music, which was entirely made up on the spot.
The saxophonist had drool coming out of his saxophone and
he would occasionally tip it up and empty all of this amassed
drool on the floor. The muscular bassist had a trimmed
moustache and sometimes he played his instrument with a
bow. At one point the drummer, who was wearing a bandana,
picked up the snare drum and bit it.

Afterwards we sat around some tables and drank vodka. The
old ladies were around and the saxophonist, whose name
was Peter, Peter something, had one of them on his lap. He
was telling a story of a friend of his, a black saxophonist
from South Africa, who he had toured with a few years back.
This guy was a drinker, and a voracious drug taker, not to
mention the carousing, he said. Muntu, was his name, Peter
said. He had put Muntu on the train in Wuppertal and had
said he would see him in a week in Paris for their next show.
Only but he never makes it. Muntu, that is. This guy Muntu
waited till I left the station, Peter said, and then he leapt
off the train and went to a pawn shop where he pawned his
saxophone. Then he toured the gay bars till he was penniless.
He shook his head in awe and amazement. One time on tour,
Peter said, he got his cock stuck in a bottle of Vosene and

he had to cut it off with a razor blade. Not his cock?! the old
lady who was on his lap asked him, an old lady by the name
of Charlotte. No, the Vosene bottle, Peter explained. How
do you know? Charlotte asked him. I mean, did he tell you a
thing like that? No, Peter said, I saw it. What?! He came out
of the shower in a panic with this bottle on his knob and he
said he had got his cock stuck in a bottle of Vosene. He said
he was trying to shampoo his balls, Peter said, and everyone
burst out laughing. He asked me to cut it off for him but no
way, Peter said, how do I know where the Vosene bottle ends
and the cock begins, I'll end up stabbing him or cutting it
off, and besides I didn't want to have to grip it, so I said to
him, only you can feel where your cock is, it's safer if you do
it, only but then neither of us had a pair of scissors and so
we settled on a single razor blade, which he had to cut deep
enough into the Vosene bottle to free his cock only but not
deep enough to gouge his penis, and inevitably, he cuts it, he
pushes down too hard and he cuts right into it and it starts
bleeding, through all this Vosene, so that there is thick pink
gunk coming out this fucking shampoo bottle around his still-
erect cock, I might add, and he looks up at me – he is sat in a
dressing gown on a stool in this miserable bed and breakfast
in Dublin – and he says to me, living the dream, huh, and
honestly it was the saddest thing anyone ever said to me,
Peter said.

Everyone had wanted to laugh at the Vosene bottle but now
it just seemed so sad. One of the old ladies sat next to me put
her arm in mine and gave an exaggerated shiver. She was
blonde and had a posh English accent. Her name was Suzy.

SUZY

You come to the foot of this pass, it is like a great granite
cube with a single daredevil path hacked out of it. We'll

never make it, this shit was made for donkeys and barefoot pilgrims, not hippies in Land Rovers, Simon says. Oh ye of little faith, Boz says. And he lights a little joint. We can do this, he says. Tell me, he says, what's your favourite rude word, he asks Simon, as he passes him the jay. Mmm . . . probably plamf, Simon says. Plamf?! Boz bursts. Plamf is your all-time favourite rude word? What's a plamf? Boz asks him and oh my God you can't believe it, I cannot believe you guys are talking about plamfs, you say, that is like my all-time favourite word never mind swear words. As in, he was a total plamf. What does it mean then? Boz asks you. It means someone who sniffs dirty knickers, you tell him, and then you realise, you are on the path, that Boz has driven straight up the face of this damn monolithic pass through the heart of this mountain without a second thought while he has been distracting you with plamf jokes because Boz is the best dude ever. Can I have a hit? you ask Simon. Didn't know you partook, Simon says, so rude of me. You and Boz catch each other's eye. Now and then, you say. Now Boz is teaching you both. Never hook your thumbs around the steering wheel in a situation like this, in a situation like what, you are asking, 'cause you are all cute-stoned and oblivious, in a situation involving plamfs, you ask him, and you and Simon both crack up, and what should you do, pray tell, should you encounter said plamf on your dirty knickers, you are asking him, but the reason you don't hook your thumbs around the steering wheel, he says, is that if you go down a hole, if your wheel catches in a ditch, this steering wheel is going to whip out of control, and you will end up with two broken thumbs, wow, Boz is so smart, Boz is so smart, isn't he Simon, yes, Simon laughs, he is a legend just like I told you, he is so smart right now, and you look out the window and it is like you are driving up the very stairwell of what is that Aztec ruin where they made all the sacrifices, exactly that, and up ahead is what looks like this great yawning cave mouth, this huge dark cave that they have driven this insane road through, and at points you run backwards, and have to pull off to the side, and try again, and eventually Boz tries reversing, wait a minute, he says, let's take this backwards, and you are both laughing at plamfs and taking it backwards and Boz is in such good spirits, even as it occurs to you that you could just as well die reversing up this rubble-strewn colossus with a gradient that feels as close to vertical as gravity will allow and yet it's all *so easy*, all *such fun*, with Boz in the car. BOZ.

THE·TOWER

16. THE TOWER

ADAM

What also helped me is swimming, swimming in the secret
rivers of West Berlin, the cold water was what helped me.
Pony's idea, of course. He had an idea where if we could
improve performance even by 1 per cent in any area of our
life then when they all came together we could beat anyone.
We must learn to swim in cold, filthy rivers, he said, as he
led me down beneath a concrete flyover where someone had
written the words '*Die Welt*'. Today is Die Welt Day, Pony
said to me, and I said, what, and he said, nothing, then he
ordered me to strip and to dive in. There were splinters of
wood floating on the water and glass bottles and plastic bags
and God knows what else. I think there might even have
been syringes on the ground. Get in it, he said. It stinks, I
said, I'll probably catch something from it, and he said to me,
you have to pierce the veil, he said. The veil of what? I asked
him. The veil of yourself, he said, and he shrugged, as if it
was obvious, and I took a look at that dirty brown water, who
knows what lies beneath, and I closed my eyes, and I held my
breath, and I jumped in. And I never touched bottom.

And it was so cold, I thought about how you could feel your
own body all at once, though really what you were feeling was
the water, the cold water gifting you the shape of your own
body, all at once, and how the cold water was your opponent,
your twin that allows you to experience yourself, but still
I couldn't open my eyes, even as I began to rise, I couldn't
open my eyes until I broke the surface, and I felt like I would
freeze, half submerged like that, forever. But Pony cheered,
and so did Coy, who I forgot to say was also there, or maybe
he just turned up, and who offered me his hand and said,
we've come a long way, and I looked back at that foul muddy

river as they pulled me out, and I thought to myself *matter is a mirror* and it felt like a revelation.

SUZY

When Boz gets too excited he has to drop down and do fast push-ups. You are finding this out now because he is so exhilarated at clearing that crazy pass that he has leapt out, into the dark, into the terrible dark of this dark cave running right through this mad mountain, its unimaginable roof hidden somewhere in its terrible darkness, and he is doing push-ups, I'm too excited, he is explaining, breathlessly, as he powers through another twenty. I told you he was a legend, is all Simon can say; he is stoned out of his gourd. Get back in the car, Boz, this endless cave is freaking me out, you tell him, and he makes the concession of just another twenty. Sorry, Duchess, he says, when he gets back in, I just get so excited sometimes, he explains. The light seems terribly far away. There must be bats and ghouls and all sorts of terrors hung upside down from its interminable heights. We need to go easy, Boz explains, we need to take it slow. You can barely see in front of yourselves. Check it out, Boz says, and he passes you a flashlight. There appear to be tunnels, snaking off, to the left and the right. My God, you could lose yourself in here, Boz says. So fucking cool, he says. You don't even want to imagine what is down those tunnels. Then you start to feel a panic, what if there is a great drop in the path, what if we stumble onto the lip of a great chasm and are cast in, car and all. What a shudder of a thought you are thinking right then as you creep along in this impenetrable darkness with only a tiny speck of light up ahead!

THE (LOVELY) STAR

17. THE (LOVELY) STAR

ADAM

We're building up to an exhibition bout, for all of the local
gang heads. They want to see how good their money is.
Now I'm practising fighting with a blindfold on. Pony has a
system of numbers that relate to certain moves, and we're
doing pads, and I have a blindfold around my head, but then
Coy says, but won't the other corner be able to figure out,
probably, the particular combinations from the numbers,
and Pony says, well, I have mixed up the numbers, so it's
unlikely, but Coy says, it's unlikely, sure, but according
to this 1-per-cent improvement scheme you have us on, I
think we should move to make it impossible, and Pony says,
okay, so, what's your idea, and Coy says, let me think for a
minute, and then he says, okay, so now we have to change the
numbers into insects, he says, and then he says, first four:
one is bug, two is beetle (of course we both smiled at that
one and there was a moment of good companionship), three
is worm, and four is slater, but Pony says, what is a slater,
and Coy says, it's a bug that lives in piles of clothes poles in
your garden, and Pony says, no, I don't want to announce the
name slater, why can't we give them names of snakes, like
black mamba, he says, rattler, cobra killer, and Coy says, let
me think for a minute, but then he says, no, and he shakes
his head and says, too obvious, that's like coming into the
ring to *Also sprach Zarathustra*, and even though none of the
two of us knew what in the hell he was going on about, we
both nodded, and said, fair enough, because we didn't want
to look like the kind of naive pansies who would use *Also
sprach Zarathustra* as their intro music, and then he says,
okay, Pony says, but if we can make slater centipede for four,
I'd really appreciate it, and but Coy says, wait, let me think
this through, he says, and then he says, too many syllables,

he says, one or two syllables only, and Pony says, what in the fuck is a syllable, and Coy says, it's a stress, like how many sounds do you have to make to make the word, cen-ti-pede, he says, that's three syllables, Coy says, and he breaks it down like that, and Pony says, okay, I hear you, plus if we keep it at two or one then nobody suspects it might be a stand-in for four or five, he says, no clues in syllables, I hear you, old man, he says to Coy, and that stung, even though it was meant with affection, that Coy could be an old man already in this story, and Pony shouts out, bug, beetle, worm, maggot, and at first it is the opposite of the cold water and the body of your opponent. At first it feels like no body at all. I'm swinging into this endless darkness, there is no one else out there. Maggot, worm, beetle, he calls out, and there is nothing, and it is endless, and it is dark. What is the shape of the dark? And then I realised it is body shaped. The dark is the shape of my body, maggot, bug, he says, and I make contact, on maggot I make contact, and I feel maggot stagger, bug, beetle, bug, and it's like I am fighting my way through a plague, a plague of black flying insects, and then he says, scarab, and at first it's a shock, but I know he means six, and I remember the scarab beetle, rolling the midnight sun, like a ball of excrement, back into the east, through the underworld, and I think to myself, for a second, that I have been trapped in this underworld for as long as I can remember, and Pony turns to Coy and says, we're wakening the warrior in him.

SUZY

You pull up at a lake, a joyous lake reveals itself at the end of that interminable drive through the cave from hell. And you are so exhilarated, everyone is so exhilarated, that you all spontaneously tear your clothes off and go running towards this lake, and leap in head first, which was foolhardy, as Simon cuts his shin on the rocks at the bottom and there is a streak of blood in the water, but who cares, the water is wonderful, and ice cold, in the shade of this mountain, in these beautiful green pasturelands in the mountains, if a magic garden tended by a blind woman is going to be anywhere, Boz says, it is in these damn hills. Then he says to you, let me flip you. What? Let me flip you, Duchess, he says. Here, he says, and he links both his hands together. Put your foot in my hand and I will raise you up and you can flip into the water. Backwards if you like. What? I couldn't possibly flip backwards, you tell him. Really? he says. And Simon starts the chant: Suzy, Suzy! Okay, you say, let's try. Only I'm nervous, you say. Don't be nervous, Boz says, there's no one in these mountains to see you. Besides, I'm the one that's gonna flip you, all you need to do is spin around in the air. That's all? That's all. Now put your hands on my shoulders, he says.

You put your hands on Boz's scrawny, tanned shoulders and you put your right foot in his hands and slowly he starts to raise you up out of the water, higher, and higher, and then you let go, you let go of his shoulders and you straighten your arms to balance yourself. A cooling wind blows your hair across your face. Suzy, Suzy! Higher and higher, out of the water. Are you ready? Yes, you are ready. Flip me. And he lifts you up, and he throws you, like a bright bird back into the air, and you turn, and twist in the air, you perform a perfect cartwheel in the air, and at the end, the perfect dive. Suzy, Suzy!

XVIIII

THE · MOON

18. THE MOON

ADAM

This fucking sorry-ass motherfucker they have set you up
with, Pony is saying. I feel sorry for his sorry motherfucking
ass, he says. I thought it was just an exhibition bout, I say to
him, I thought we were just there to show off a bit. My friend,
he says, but just exactly who the fuck do you think you're
kidding? I shrugged, and Coy shrugged, too, when I looked
round at him, though I could see that he looked worried. You
are there to destroy this sorry-ass motherfucker's ass. You
are there to fuck his shit up. Both gangs are watching, with
interest, I might add. This is a fucking cockfight, my brother,
he said, as he was strapping my hands. What's his story? Coy
asked him. They call him The Head, Pony said. He's hip. But
he's out of his depth. Pony is strapping up my hands because
he has me punching coconuts that he bought at the Somali
market. What's his style? Coy asked him. Evasive, Pony said,
exhaustive, long-game, mental warfare, intimidation and
goading, getting under you, under your chin, beneath your
skin. Okay, Coy said, let me think for a minute, and then
he said, we come in hard and we annihilate this fucker in
the first few rounds. We don't play his game. It's not about
defence, it's about breaching, Pony agreed. Only but I just
found out that he is left-handed. What? me and Coy groaned
at the same time, but Pony said, all we have to do is invert
everything that we have learned. Wait, no, we don't want to
invert it, Coy said, surely we want to flip it? Flip it, invert
it, see it sideways, that's the way, Pony said, as he tied my
gloves and held a coconut on a rope in front of me and said,
this is The Head, he said, this is the motherfucking Head
right here, and I cracked it open with one punch and all of
this gunk fell out and of course everyone made another joke
about Muntu.

On the night they had this ring set up in an interior
courtyard, it was the summer in Berlin, and all the old ladies
were there, and there was a wild crowd, a lot of hippies,
and bikers, and radicals, but first they had a science-fiction
writer, some science-fiction nut, up onstage and he read some
poems about utopia and terraforming, was the word he used,
what the fuck is terraforming on Mars, I said to Pony, and he
said, making other planets habitable, and I said, huh, okay,
and then I caught a glimpse of Suzy and I made my way over,
she was working in this little improvised kitchen area they
had set up, she was cooking and serving vegetarian meals,
and I went over to her and I ordered two plates of patatas
bravas, because for some reason the menu was all Spanish-
style, this was for Coy and for Pony, all I was eating was
chicken and rice at this point, and she served me one portion
but I kept standing there, waiting for the other one, until
she said to me, what are you waiting for, and I said, well, the
second order, and she said, oh, sorry, I didn't hear you order
two, she said, I thought you just wanted to see me, she said,
and she made me blush, then, but then this guy came up and
grabbed her and I realised they were a bit of an item, this guy
called La Mort, this tough biker with a bandana on his head
and a long, thin beard and a red face and tattoos, and Suzy
was embarrassed, and she said that I had offered to read her
and La Mort's tarot cards, even though I hadn't, even though
I didn't know what a tarot card even was then, but I could tell
she was covering our tracks, while building a secret alliance,
and he said, oh yeah, and he looked at me suspiciously, like
he was buying none of it, and so I said, yeah, man, I should
do your cards sometime, and La Mort said, I don't do that
shit, man, he said, I'm working magic every minute, he said, I
don't need to check the stats, and then he put his hands down
the front of Suzy's dress and started fingering her, roughly,
and I grabbed the snacks and headed backstage, but not
before I caught Spidey playing a live acoustic set in the ring

where he sang a song about understanding the meaning of
space and time and played a harmonica solo that lasted an
eternity.

I came backstage with my patatas bravas. Boxing is the new
rock 'n' roll, Pony shrugged, and he and Coy cracked open a
beer and got stuck into the potatoes. You seen our guy yet? I
asked them. We've seen him, Coy nodded, and Pony nodded,
too. Well? He's dead meat, Pony said, and he bit into this
spicy potato thing so that the red sauce was all drooling down
his chin and he looked like he had taken a bite out of this
loser's motherfucking neck. You look like you have just taken
a bite out of this loser's motherfucking neck, I said to him,
and as he washed it down with a beer he said, yeah, man, I'll
dress his asshole and feed it to my children, he said, and I
thought, what the fuck is he on about, but who cares, 'cause
it's brilliant.

SUZY

You return to find your Land Rover gone. Someone in these
idyllic fucking mountains has stolen your fucking Land
Rover. Fuck, Boz, says, fuck, fuck, fuck, never leave your
keys with the car in Afghanistan in the fucking mountains
all alone is rule number one, he says, I'm a fucking amateur,
he says, fuck, fuck, fuck. They left our bags, wait, where's my
bag? Boz says. Fuck, they took my fucking bag. What was in
it? you ask him. Money, he says. And heroin. A substantial
amount of heroin. We could be in a shitload of trouble here,
he says, but then he points out how you are all stood around
naked. Wow, we are just stood around naked talking about
this, he says, this is weird. I kind of like it, he says, this
kind of naked talk. But you gather up your clothes and get
dressed all the same. I guess we have no choice but to walk,
Simon says, and Boz can find his way by the sun, he says,

and suggests you head north-east along this spectacular
green ridge with the desert down below, and through fields of
flowers, you descend across fields of flowers to a valley with a
stream running through it and then up the other side, where
there is smoke in the distance, a habitation, Boz says, he is
talking like a true guide, as you approach this little stone
habitation, it's true, like the first house at the beginning
of the world, and it is true you are starting to feel unwell,
is it the heroin withdrawal, and Boz stands outside this
ancient stone habitation from the dawn of time and calls out
something beautiful in Persian, it really is extraordinarily
lovely, and a woman comes to the door at the call of this
lovely voice, this beautiful language, who says her name is
Madini, how is this possible, and she is blind, she is blind
and appears to have a garden. She asks Boz something and
points towards you. What did she say? She asked if you are
in mourning, he says, she asked whether someone had died.
She is asking, what is that weight? You reach into your bag
and put on the black feather headdress that Aifa gifted you.
Madini comes towards you and puts her hands to either side
of your head and as she strokes your feathers she says, my
beautiful bird, my daughter, come back to me, in purring
Persian, so beautifully.

THE • SUN

19. THE SUN

ADAM

I don't remember the fight. I don't remember it at all. It was my first fight without amphetamines. They fucking drug-tested us. I was so anxious. I did my thing where I ran around the block six or seven times, this deserted-looking block that was all graffitied and run-down and with broken windows in Berlin. I hadn't cracked one off in weeks. My balls ached. And then my memory goes.

I'm in the back of a car with Suzy and La Mort and Spidey and Pony. Where's Coy? I ask them but nobody answers and instead Spidey starts singing 'Wild Thing'. Everyone is smoking joints and passing round a bottle of champagne. That's right, I remember, I won, I won. Only but the guy is in a fucking coma. The Head. The Head is in a coma. Fuck that loser bitch, La Mort says. It is twilight for him, he says, forever.

We get to this club, this scene, this Happening. They are smashing TVs onstage, a naked couple are smashing live TVs onstage with sledgehammers, and on the TV there is a film about beetles, about beetles taking over the world, and it's too weird. Pony, I say, Pony, what was the combo I won it on, and he says, you mean you can't remember, and I say to him, I took some blows to the head, I feel a little shaky, I feel a little confused, I say to him, and he says to me, you barely took a single hit to the head, you fucking dope, you annihilated that sorry-ass motherfucker, and I said, but how, I don't remember, and Pony said, beetle, beetle, grub, grub, grub. And I thought, what's grub? But I said nothing, except I said, grub, huh, and Pony nodded and repeated it, grub, grub, grub, he said, and then Spidey put his arm around me and said, you're the main man tonight, he said, what's it gonna be, and I said, I want to make love to Suzy, I said to him, I've got a thing for Suzy, I said, and he said, she's La Mort's old lady, he said, and he's possessive as fuck, he said, so that's not going to happen and even if it does I wouldn't advise it, he said, and then he said, choose from any old lady, he said, and he gestured around the room as if he was offering it all to me, just stay away from Suzy, would be my advice, but first, he said, you want a line? I've been looking for a line all night, I said, I thought there was a drought, and Spidey said, no, man, you don't understand, this is prime white mosquito, he said, and I swear I almost ducked, white mosquito, he said, and as he led me into the toilets some old lady said to us, do you guys got coke, and I took her hand, and I said, come with me, and I said to her, I want you to lick it off my forehead, I said, and the next thing I remember is I am sat on the can while Spidey blocks the door and this girl licks lines of coke from my forehead while all the time Spidey kept repeating, curl that little tongue, baby, that's right, lick up that good white, and she sat on my lap, and I held her, on this toilet, as she ran her cool tongue, while she curled her face like a sneer, and I said, Spidey, do me a favour and get the fuck out of here, and he said, sure, you're the boss tonight, boss, and when he left Angela stood up and bent over me on the toilet bowl and sucked my engorged cock and put her fingers down my throat at the same time until I came, choking.

And then there's a blank again. And then there's this . . . thing. There's this thing stood in front of me and it is a headless bird, a headless black bird reared up on its hind legs like a man in a black shroud, and it offers its wing to me, and I take it under my arm, and we don't so much take off as are propelled forward, and I think, oh my fucking God, I am reading my life like a book, or rather, I am being introduced to the book of my life, which means it is written, which means it is written by this black bird, holy fuck.

SUZY

You give birth to Alan's stillborn child in this habitation at the beginning of the world.

THE•AEON

20. THE AEON

ADAM

I ask this black headless bird, why do they call them flower children? Because they have their roots in darkness. Because they come for the nectar and leave bearing seeds. Because they sigh in the wind. Because they. Because they have a season. Because their place is in the sun. Write this down, this black bird commanded, because they are in league with the worms. Here, write this down. The Beatles, in the grass, are commanded. I am writing this down.

SUZY

Simon and Boz help you bury Alan and Suzy's unborn daughter beneath a tree, in the middle of this garden, on a magic mountain, somewhere. Silently, you name her Suzy. There is a great well in this garden, an impossibly deep pool, risen up. Madini says that it is as deep as the world. I long to swim in that pool, you dream to yourself, at night, in these mountains, of diving deep into that well, and of appearing somewhere else – *begin again, begin again* – are the sounds of these waters, at night.

21. THE UNIVERSE

ADAM

A string of blackout fights follow. I can no longer retain any
memory of what happens in the ring. I am the victor, is all I
know. You're the victor, Coy would say, you're the champion,
Pony would say, and afterwards the gang would head to some
squat, some underground club – the Optic, the Shattered
Nerve, Zeroes – and there would be these spectacular light
shows, these wicked blooms that matched the feeling I had
in my brain, this seed point of death, blazing suddenly, of
waking up again, and again, as the victor.

I went out of my way to be around Suzy. I was getting respect
from La Mort, he wasn't as suspicious, and plus, he knew I
was a blackout killer in the ring, so he backed off. I bought a
set of tarot cards from Kicking Bear's. Hold one of them up
but don't let me see it, I told Pony. Then I said, The Pope, and
Pony said, they're not for guessing, that's ESP cards you are
thinking of, and I said, okay, so what do you do with them,
and he said to me, you deal out the cards and make a story
out of them that tells the future, only not really the future,
and not really the past or the present either, he said, more
like the possibilities of the moment, the possibilities of now.
I'm going to read Suzy's cards, I told him, I said I would. But
you don't know anything about reading the cards, Pony said,
and I said, won't it just be like reading the times, and Pony
shrugged and said, I guess. But then Suzy disappeared.

I would go downstairs to hang with the old ladies who
teased me and called me Speedy Gonzales and they joked,
I think you are a little in love with Suzy, they said, and I
would protest and say, well, I wouldn't say I was in love,
and they would all tease me again and shout, see, only

a man in love wouldn't refute it, and one girl was a folk singer called Marnie, and one of them was a witch who worshipped a knotted tree trunk in the park that had been hit by lightning, she was called Valerie, and Carrie ran the kitchen, even though it was a communal kitchen, supposedly, but in reality the old ladies ran it, and they would make me soup while the rain fell on the long apartment windows and the deserted streets, and after several months Suzy hadn't returned and La Mort hadn't been seen, either, and though no one else seemed concerned, I began to get a bad feeling, that somehow that black bird was someone dead coming back to me, that I had been in conversation with a disappeared ghost, and then Marnie told me that there was a rumour that he had defected, that La Mort had gone across to the fucking Trots because something big was about to go down, some kind of action, because Red Force, which was the secret name of the revolutionary cell the hippies that kidnapped me were involved in, Red Force were all fucking talk at this point, was the rumour, that they were basically a gang of hedonists without the first motherfucking clue about class consciousness, was the rumour, on the underground, she said, and sure enough it was true, the next week an incendiary device went off at a department store in Charlottenburg-Wilmersdorf and the PGM, the People's Guns and Minds, claimed responsibility. They pulled body parts from the rubble, but all that was left were ashes, really, and so they were never identified, but then Suzy and La Mort were never heard from again, and Marnie told me, it was them, the PGM confirmed that they had been sent out on a mission to burn this department store to the motherfucking ground and never returned.

I am reading Suzy's tarot for her. I am writing it for a black bird.

SUZY

A party of armed security men stormed this perfect garden
in the mountains in search of the motherfuckers who were
smuggling heroin and there was a stand-off, and then a
shoot-out. Simon is dead, Boz, missing, Madini; it is as if she
never existed. To the sound of automatic weapons, and in the
destruction of this garden, you make for the pool that is as
deep as this world.

((surf music plays))

POSTSCRIPT: INDUSTRY

INTERVIEW WITH EFFIE DARROW IN *SPEX* MAGAZINE

Effie Darrow is one half of the brains behind Azazrael: Play
Hard, the cult computer game programmers who brought
us BBC, ZX Spectrum, VIC-20 and Commodore 64 text-
only adventures like *Headquarters: Daath, Monolith Out of
Space* and *Return to Eden* as well as the classic games *Space
Station, Turbulence* and *The Rise of Ma'at*. Interviewed by
Don Robertson.

> Don: How did you get the idea for *Space Station*?
> Effie: I imagined a station floating in space and then I
> imagined it getting invaded.
> Don: How did you get the idea for *Return to Eden*?
> Effie: I imagined returning to Eden and it was all
> overgrown and out of control in our absence.
> Don: How did you get the idea for *The Rise of Ma'at*?
> Effie: Well, Ma'at is the Feather of Truth.
> Don: What is the message of the headless birds in
> *Headquarters: Daath*?
> Effie: Seen from below, in flight, the saints can seem as
> headless birds.
> Don: What is your favourite game?

Effie: Russian Roulette.

Don: In *Return to Eden* is it possible to cross the river by throwing the rope?

Effie: It is possible, but it has to be phrased in a certain way.

Don: What was your inspiration for Azazrael: Play Hard?

Effie: The Battle of Katherine Park.

Don: BBC? ZX81?

Effie: Airdrie, 1971. When mounted police attacked a peaceful rock festival.

Don: What do you think the next step in games is?

Effie: Interactive. Interactive with other human beings, all exploring this phantom landscape, together, like scrying the blood tree or the patrolling of the Aethers.

Don: In *Turbulence* is there a secret key sequence that unlocks a subterranean level?

Effie: Yes.

Don: Can you tell us what it is?

Effie: No. But someone must know, otherwise who realised there was a subterranean level to the game? I never told.

Don: Who made the music for the games? Is it all the same person?

Effie: Yes, TOBIAS. He's kind of a new-age synth legend.

Don: What is Azazrael?

Effie: Keeper of the Bones.

Don: In *Monolith Out of Space* is it actually possible to escape from the maze if you accidentally wander into it?

Effie: No. The maze is, intentionally, fathomless.

Don: Do you think Buddhists literally experience a different reality?

Effie: I wouldn't know, I'm not a Buddhist.

Don: Does knowing that all this is a manifestation of consciousness, uprising, and disappearing, from nothing, into nothing, for no one, mean that your experience of reality changes?

Effie: That's not what you asked. You asked me if Buddhists literally experience a different reality. Now you are asking if it is the perception of that reality that is changed.

Don: Well?

Effie: *(laughs)* Well what?

Don: Well, so, why does consciousness switch on and off?

Effie: What do you mean?

Don: At death, why does consciousness come and go?

Effie: Well, who says it does?

Don: The dead don't come back.

Effie: That doesn't refute the continuity of consciousness. And besides, they do.

Don: You ever go dumpster diving up at Organon?

Effie: Oh yeah, sure, that was where we got most of the early mainframe manuals.

Don: Yeah, me too, how come I never bumped into you?

Effie: The bins round the back of Organon weren't exactly the busiest hotspot, Don. Besides, I was a hippy, you would have hated me.

Don: Probably. Anyway. How do you feel when you hear the words 'Illegal Format' and 'Illegal Access'?

Effie: I think of Hewlett-Packard's HP 2000. I feel romantic. My favourite is green digital text against black, with a flashing cursor, in the middle of the night.

Don: You always hack at night?

Effie: Pretty much all night.

Don: Me too.

Effie: Did you realise that many of the original phone phreaks were blind?

Don: Yes, I remember when I heard that I thought, well, this makes perfect sense.

Effie: What is it they say about how when one sense
    atrophies the other expands, in compensation?
Don: You know Joybubbles?
Effie: Yeah, Joybubbles, what a name, this is this blind kid
    who could recognise all of the frequencies needed to
    communicate on the phone networks by ear and so who
    was making alla these free calls.
Don: And of course Cap'n Crunch got his name because he
    found this whistle that you got free in boxes of Cap'n
    Crunch cereal that emitted the exact frequency that
    triggered operator mode on AT&T phone lines.
Effie: You hate hippies but this is exactly the ethos that I
    took out of hippiedom, that whatever you need, at any
    time, is right there in front of you, if only you had the
    imagination to recognise it.
Don: Favourite home computer?
Effie: BBC Micro. Hands down. I remember seeing it
    getting displayed in the basement of John Smith's
    bookshop in Glasgow and just swooning. That
    keyboard. That monitor. That logo. (Swoons.) The
    future.
Don: Talking about the future, is there anything still to be
    done after psychedelic music and punk? I know you
    were involved with the psychedelic scene back in the
    day. What's interesting that's happening now? You
    think rock music has anywhere left to go?
Effie: Yes, and they're called Memorial Device.
Don: Let's talk about different realities.
Effie: All realities are manmade.
Don: In as much as all realities take place in consciousness.
Effie: All strategies that create new realities are further
    methods of ingress.
Don: What's the most efficacious form of magick?
Effie: Scrying, mirror magic, books, technology.
Don: In that order?

Effie: Not necessarily.

Don: What were the headless birds that were seen, in the skies, over Airdrie, in the early 1970s?

Effie: During our workings, headless birds appeared. They had names beginning with A that I am no longer willing to speak.

Don: They told you their names?

Effie: You can't have traffic with demons and angels without knowledge of the name to call them.

Don: And what had they come to do?

Effie: They had come to deliver a book of revelation, they told us.

Don: And what was the name of this book?

Effie: *Industry of Magic & Light*.